Gold Stars

THIRD GRADE
BIG WORKBOOK

Parragon.

Helping Your Child

- Remember that the activities in this book should be enjoyed by your child. Try to find a quiet place to work.

- Always give your child lots of encouragement and praise.

- Your child does not need to complete each page in one go. Always stop before your child grows tired, and come back to the same page another time.

- The answers to the activities are on pages 307–320.

This edition published by Cottage Door Press, LLC, in 2021.

Copyright © 2021 Cottgae Door Press, LLC
5005 Newport Drive, Rolling Meadows, Illinois 60008

Page 132 Photo courtesy of Library of Congress, Rare Book and Special Collections Division, National American Woman Suffrage Association Collection.

Written by Nina Filipek and Michael Ward
Cover art by Irina Avvakumova, used under licence from Shutterstock.com
Illustrated by Simon Abbott, Adam Linley, and Helen Prole
Educational Consultant: Cassandra Hames

ISBN: 978-1-64638-167-8

Printed in China

Gold Stars™ is an imprint of Cottage Door Press, LLC.
Parragon Books® and the Parragon® logo are registered trademarks of Cottage Door Press, LLC.

Contents

Spelling and Vocabulary

Helping Your Child

- The activities in this section will help your child to learn how to spell a variety of common words, including nouns, verbs, adjectives, and compound words.

- Your child will learn how to identify word beginnings (prefixes) and word endings (suffixes), and how these can change the meaning of words.

- Children learn to spell by reading and writing. If your child finds a word difficult to spell, try to follow this method: LOOK at the word; COVER UP the word; WRITE the word; CHECK the word.

- Set aside time to do the activities together. Do a little at a time, so that your child enjoys learning.

- The answers begin on page 307.

Contents

Consonants and Vowels

There are five vowels in the alphabet. The other 21 letters are consonants. Find the vowels on the balloons and color them in.

How many words can you make out of the letters on the balloons?

out

the

cop

get

lase

Shout

tea

pot

Pick

Underline the vowels in each of your words.
List the consonants not seen on the balloons.

Note for parent: The vowels (a, e, i, o, u) are different to consonants because of how we say them. Sometimes y is a vowel in words like why and cry.

Short Vowel Sounds

Each of these words has a short (or hard) vowel sound.
Say them out loud.

d**o**g	b**u**g	fr**ie**nd	s**a**nd
b**e**d	s**o**cks	g**i**ft	br**ea**d

Choose a word from above to complete each sentence.

1. The .... chewed up my sister's teddy bear.

2. When I go to the beach I always get ....

in my .... !

3. My best .... likes to play the violin.

4. I spotted a big .... crawling underneath my ....

5. I went to the shop to buy a .... for my mom.

6. My brother ate all the .... so there was none left

for my sandwich!

Note for parent: Short vowel sounds have a hard sound when pronounced, whereas long vowel sounds are softer.

7

Long Vowel Sounds

Write the missing vowel letters to spell these words.

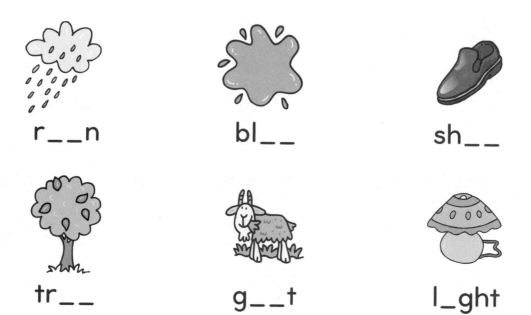

r__n   bl__   sh__

tr__   g__t   l_ght

These words have a long vowel sound. Say them out loud.

Read the poem. Underline the long vowel sounds.

There is a man who lives on the moon

He eats cheese with a big blue spoon.

He likes it up there where the stars shine bright,

They never go in; it is always night.

We could drop by for a nice cup of tea,

So, let's take a trip—just you and me!

Note for parent: Words in the poem with long vowel sounds include: moon, eats, cheese, blue, spoon, likes, shine, bright, night, nice, tea, me.

Ending Blends

Add the correct ending to spell these words.

ct	pt	th

perfe__   nin__   obje__   cre__

four__   subje__   stri__   swe__

seven__   eru__

Choose words from the above list to help finish this set of instructions.

1. Go south from the volcano that is about to ....

2. When you reach the .... palm tree, go west.

3. Follow the trail past the .... lake.

4. There are three statues. But only one is ....

5. The treasure is buried in front of it.

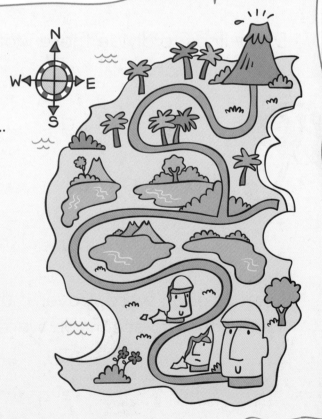

Note for parent: This activity will help your child to review consonant blends at the end of words.

Spelling Techniques

You can break a long word into smaller parts, called syllables.

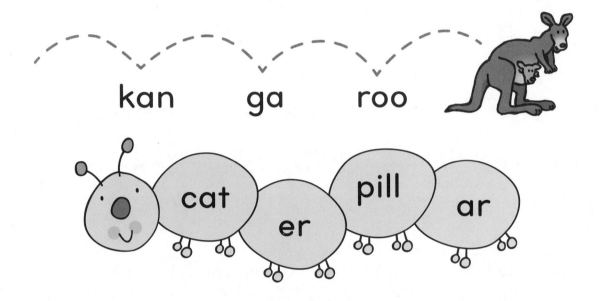

kan   ga   roo

cat   er   pill   ar

Draw lines to divide these words into syllables.

u m b r e l l a   c r o c o d i l e

t o r n a d o   d i n o s a u r

Look at each word. Cover it up. Then write it on a line below. Then check to see if you were right.

....

....

Note for parent: Remind your child to practice the look, cover, write, check method to spell other words in this book.

Using a Dictionary

A dictionary can help you spell words.
Words in a dictionary are in alphabetical order.
Help Emma put these words in alphabetical order.

snail

blanket

cowboy

picture

pirate

block

black

snake

1. ....

2. ....

3. ....

4. ....

5. ....

6. ....

7. ....

8. ....

Use a dictionary to check your answers.

Note for parent: Remind your child that sometimes they need to look at the second, third, or fourth letter of a word (and so on) to decide its order.

11

Spelling Patterns

Look for patterns in sounds and spellings. These words belong to a group called a word family.

b**itter**	fr**itter**	cr**itter**	l**itter**

Read the words in the bubbles. Draw lines to join the word families.

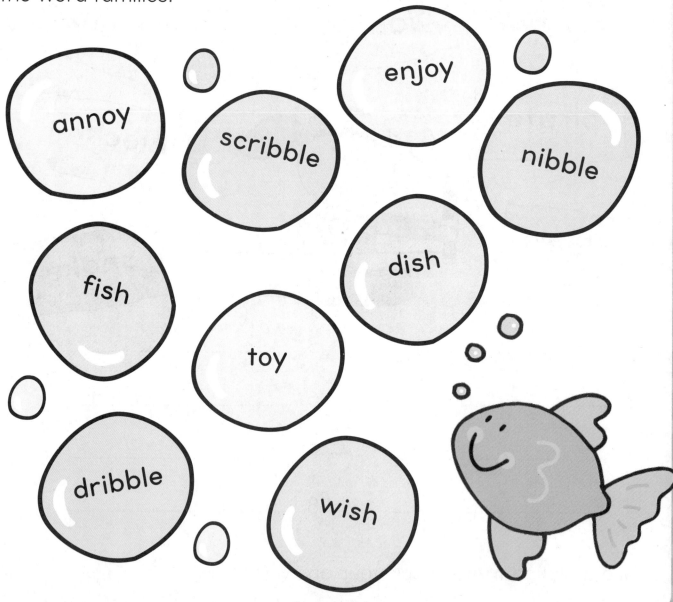

Note for parent: When spelling an unfamiliar word, help your child to blend the sounds and compare with other words that they know.

Tricky Words

Some words are not spelled how they sound. Read and try to remember what these tricky words look like.

because	people	early	biscuit
heard	through	who	their

Cover up the words. Then choose the correct spelling for each sentence.

1. I woke up (**early** / **earlie**) today (**because** / **beecos**) I am going on vacation.

2. The (**peeple** / **people**) were pushing and pulling to get (**thruw** / **through**) the store's doors.

3. I like to give my dog a (**biscit** / **biscuit**) before I go to bed.

4. I (**heard** / **herd**) that it is not (**who** / **whu**) you know, but what you know.

13

Rhyming Words

Draw a line to all the words that rhyme with the word in the circle.

rise

those

ring

nose

goes

throws

rose

lose

race

beat

neat

sweet

feet

street

cheat

feel

set

float

ear

pale

square

stare

pear

fear

chair

pearl

bear

Note for parent: Emphasize the sounds of the words as you read them. Notice that rhyming words may sound similar but are not always spelled the same.

Missing Sounds

Read the poem. Fill in the missing sounds to complete the words.

Try not to catch a c**o**ld, my dear.

Your head will turn bl**ue**.

And your fingers, too.

Your nose will fall off,

With that very loud c**ou**gh.

You'll be stuck in b**e**d,

With an ache in your head.

What a sorry sight,

You will look a fr**iend**.

Yes, listen to Grandmother, she knows all,

So, try not to ca**tch** a cold this fall.

Note for parent: Read the poem together. Encourage your child to use clues in the text, as well as the rhyming pattern, to help them fill in the missing letter sounds.

Endings le, al, el

Choose the correct ending (**le**, **al**, **el**) for the words in these sentences.

l. Tommy came first in the swimming race and won a med_el_.

2. When we go on vacation we like to stay in a hot_el_.

3. I put a lab_el_ on the present so I know who it is for.

4. Bella reached for an app_le_ from the tree.

5. In the desert, you can ride a cam_al_.

6. On the beach, I found a shiny pebb_le_.

7. We like to sit around the tab_le_ to have our dinner.

Root Words

A root word is a word that makes new words when you add letters to it.

teach   **teach**ing   **teach**er

Underline the root word in these examples.

<u>**bake**</u>s   <u>**bake**</u>r

smaller   smallest

bravely   bravest

bicycle   tricycle

Make new words using these root words.

tall ..... tallest ..... taller

farm ..... farmer ..... farming

clever ..... clevere ..... cleverest

throw ..... throwing ..... throwing up

slow ..... slower ..... slowest

Note for parent: Letters can be added to the beginning of a root word (prefix) or the end of a root word (suffix) to make a new word.

17

Common Prefixes

A prefix is a group of letters you add to the beginning of a root word to make a new word.

place **re**place	usual **un**usual	own **dis**own

These prefixes can change the meaning of a root word—and often give an opposite meaning.

Read the text and circle all the prefixes that you can find.

Wilko the Wizard is very unhappy.

He is unable to recall the words to his

favorite spell. Perhaps you can help

him to say the words...

"Disappear, reappear, look in all the places,

For the magic whizzle that will untie my laces!"

Negative Prefixes

We have learned that prefixes can change the meaning of words. Sometimes they can give a negative or opposite meaning.

appear   **dis**appear

polite   **im**polite

Choose a prefix from the box to complete each sentence.

dis   un   im   in   mis

1. It is __im__ polite to stare at someone.

2. My friend says apples are the tastiest fruit, but I __dis__ agree.

3. I couldn't __un__ do the knot, so I couldn't take my shoe off!

4. The dogs in the puppy training class were __mis__ behaving.

5. Jake got most of his answers __in__ correct, so he

had to retake the test.

Note for parent: Play an opposites game where you choose a word and your child gives you an opposite by adding a prefix. For example: happy, unhappy.

Common Suffixes ing and ed

A suffix is a letter or a group of letters you add to the end of a root word. The suffixes **ing** and **ed** change the tense of a word.

> I am paint**ing** a picture. (present tense)
>
> I paint**ed** a picture. (past tense)

We add a double letter when there is a short vowel before the final consonant.

sw_im   swim**ming**   h_op   hop**ped**

Write a sentence for each of these pictures.
Use an **ed** or **ing** word in each sentence.

.... hopped ....

.... slipped ....

.... hand wash ....

.... running ....

Note for parent: This activity gives your child practice in spelling words with the common suffixes ed and ing. Use a dictionary to check spelling.

Making New Words

Remember, you can make new words by adding a prefix.

super + star = superstar!

Link these prefixes to the words in the middle.
Then write the word you have made.

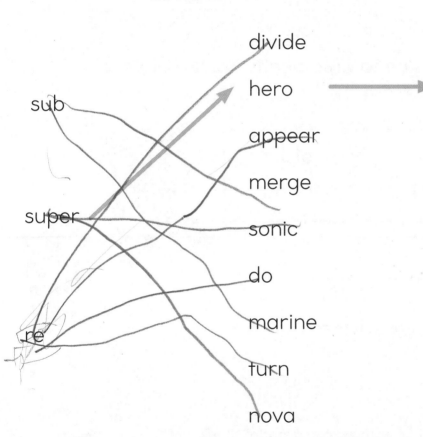

divide

hero

appear

merge

sonic

do

marine

turn

nova

sub

super

re

return
superhero
supernova
submerge
supersonic
redo
redvide
submarine
reapeor

Write three sentences using some of the words you have made.

Wow! Look at the supanova!

I have retuned!

I am a super supahero.

Note for parent: Encourage your child to use a dictionary to check their answers and to find the meanings of any words they are unfamiliar with.

Adding ly to an Adjective

When you add **ly** to an adjective you create an adverb.

adjective	adverb
sad	sad**ly**
loud	loud**ly**

Decide if these sentences need an adjective or an adverb.
Choose the missing word from the box.

bold	**foolish**	**graceful**
boldly	**foolishly**	**gracefully**

1. The painting had very ......*bold*...... colors.

2. I ......*foolishly*...... trusted my sister not to eat all the popcorn.

3. The ballerina danced ......*gracefully*...... to the music.

4. The brave knight ......*boldly*...... entered the dragon's cave.

5. It was a ......*foolish*...... risk to climb the mountain alone.

6. The swan had a long, ...*graceful*...... neck.

Note for parent: Encourage your child to think of other adjectives that they can turn into adverbs with ly. Then make a sentence with each.

Adding ly to Words Ending le or y

If a word ends in **le**, drop the **e** before adding **y**.

gentle	gently	sparkle	sparkly

If a word ends in **y**, change the **y** to an **i** then add **ly**.

sleepy	sleepily	noisy	noisily

Change these words by adding **ly**.

scary   scaryly

simple   simelely

humble   humblely

spooky   spookly

crazy   crazly

cuddle   cuddley

easy   easyly

happy   Happyly

Write a sentence using one of the words you have made.

Im Happy Hungry

Words with the Suffix ous

Look at the **ous** words in the box. Write the root word for each one.

dangerous   mountainous   courageous   famous

danger

vigorous   joyous   envious   venomous

Now find the root words in the grid below.

R	L	L	Q	V	Q	D	Y	Y	R
E	K	N	I	A	T	N	U	O	M
G	G	V	E	N	O	M	G	E	N
N	F	A	X	A	M	I	V	N	V
A	I	A	R	H	V	X	F	V	H
D	Z	J	M	U	V	X	B	Y	I
V	O	I	R	E	Q	O	H	E	T
Y	N	I	R	Q	J	C	H	H	J
S	U	O	O	I	Q	Z	P	N	L
W	I	J	C	O	R	P	U	N	T

Note for parent: Help your child make a sentence for each of the ous words you have explored.

Spell with ture and sure

Fill in the missing words to complete the poem.

nature	pleasure	treasure	picture	measure

We are the pirates—yo, ho, ho!

Sailing is our ......_pleasure_...., don't you know?

We've got lots of ......_tresure_...., coins, and jewels

Because we don't plan to follow the rules.

We buried them beneath the brightest star

But we forgot to ......_measure_.... just how far.

We should have a ......_picture_.... to help us remember,

We've been looking for it since last November.

We won't give up, it's not in our ......_natur_....

So don't laugh at us, else we're coming to get yer!

Note for parent: This activity will give your child practice in spelling words that end with ture and sure.

25

Spell with tion

Spell the word next to the correct definition.

action	invention	rotation
position	solution	fiction

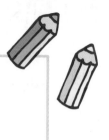

solutoin
....
the answer to a problem

fixion
....
something that is made up or untrue

Rotot *action*
....
a movement or series of movements

Position
....
a place where something is put

rotating
....
a spinning or turning motion

invention
....
something that is made
for the very first time

What order would you find those words in a dictionary?

1. ....   2. ....   3. ....

4. ....   5. ....   6. ....

Note for parent: The letters tion sound like shun when spoken aloud. Help your child to think of other words with a similar spelling and sound.

Spell with sc

Complete the crossword by solving the clues. All the words start with or have the letters **sc** in them.

Across

1. To move upward

5. To help an actor learn their lines

6. To explain something

7. A school subject

Down

2. Used for cutting

3. To move downward

4. A moon shape

7. A roll of parchment or paper

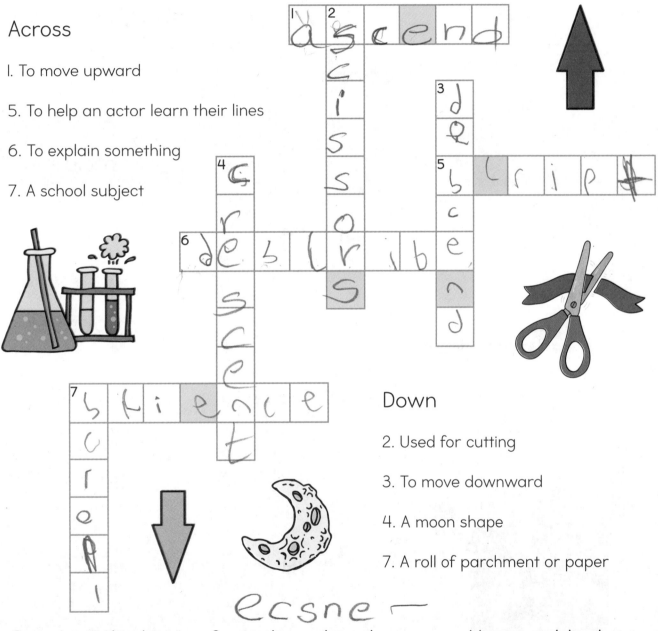

Copy out the letters from the colored squares. Unscramble them to spell another word with **sc**. scene

....

Note for parent: The letters sc can give a hard k sound as in scroll and a softer s sound if they come before a vowel, as in scenery.

29

Spell Tricky Words

Look at each word. Cover it up. Write the word on the line below.
Then check your answer.

because

....

people

....

enough

....

favorite

....

answer

....

imagine

....

although

....

different

....

important

....

necessary

....

thought

....

surprise

....

tricky
word
machine

Note for parent: There is no easy way of learning these words. But with practice and familiarity your child will begin to recognize them on sight.

Words with ei

Add **ei** to complete these words. Say them out loud. Circle the words that have the long **a** sound.

v__l   h__ght   __ght   rec__ve

w__ght   sl__gh   fr__ght   v__rd

r__ndeer   n__ghbor

Choose words from the list above to complete the sentences.

1. The bride was wearing a white ....

2. The .... train had .... carriages.

3. My .... was happy to .... the present.

4. The doctor measured my .... and ....

5. There are nine .... that pull Santa's ....

6. I had a .... dream last night.

Words with ie

Add **ie** to complete these words. Say them out loud. Circle the words that have the long **e** sound.

sh_ _ld	rel_ _f	f_ _ld	tr_ _d
cr_ _d	l_ _	br_ _f	th_ _f

Choose words from the list above to complete the poem.

The cowardly knight took to the field

With his rusty old sword and battered ....

He said:

"This fight will be .... It will end in grief.

I won't tell a .... , I'm going to die.

Wait! The giant is sleeping. That's a ....

I'm going to creep past, like a sneaky ....

At least I can say I really ....

No one will know I almost cried!"

Note for parent: The letters ie can give the long e sound as in shield and the long i sound as in lied.

Words with ou

Add **ou** to complete these words.

The terrible twins (do they ever agree?)

 I think you sh_ _ld.

Well, surely you c_ _ld.

 I thought you w_ _ld.

Oh I've had en_ _gh!

 You're far too r_ _gh!

You think you're t_ _gh!

Why are you my d_ _ble?

You are just tr_ _ble!

Note for parent: The letters ou in these words can produce the long uh sound or the short u sound. Help your child to create new sentences using these words.

Words with y in the Middle

Unscramble the letters to spell these words.

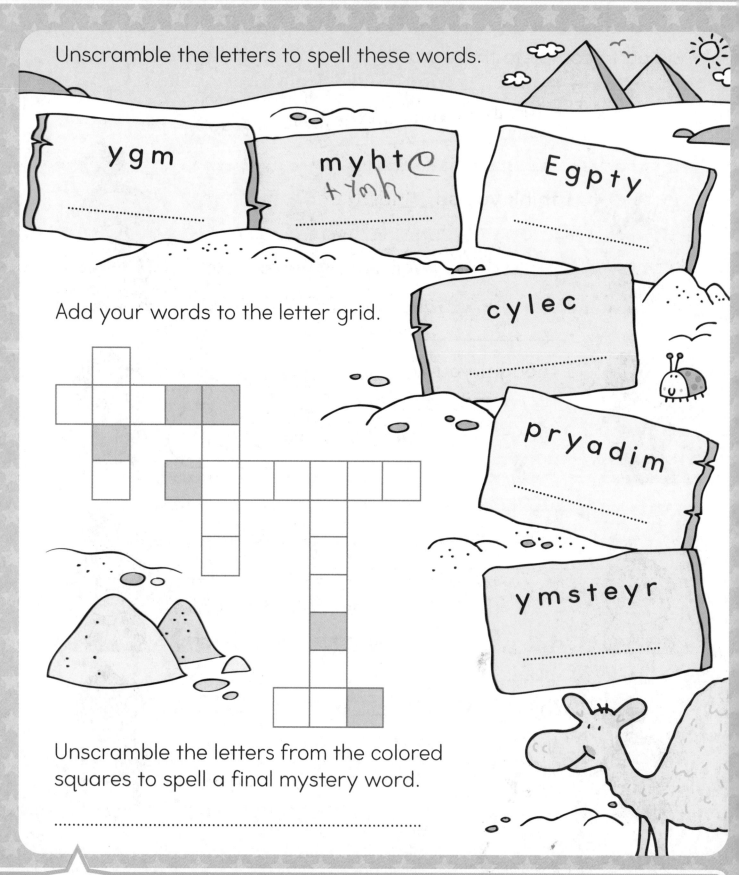

ygm

....

myhte
tymh

....

Egpty

....

cylec

....

pryadim

....

ymsteyr

....

Add your words to the letter grid.

Unscramble the letters from the colored squares to spell a final mystery word.

....

Note for parent: The letter y in the middle of a word produces the long i sound. When a vowel comes before the y then the y becomes silent, as in prayer.

Changing Verbs into Nouns

You can change a verb into a noun by adding a suffix.

Tom wants to be a (**sing**) ....singer....
when he grows up.

verb—sing   noun—sing**er**

Change each highlighted word into a noun by adding
a suffix (**er, ure, ment, ation**).

1. We got confused because we were given the wrong (**inform**) ....

2. The (**paint**) .... likes to use water colors.

3. I really hope I am not late for my hair (**appoint**) ....

4. Our flight (**depart**) .... was delayed by two hours.

5. For his (**punish**) .... , Sam had to wash the dishes.

6. The (**dine**) .... found a fly in his soup!

7. The new action movie was good (**entertain**) ....

Note for parent: This activity will give your child further practice in adding suffixes to root words. Encourage the use of a dictionary to check spelling.

35

Silent Letters

Look at the pictures and write the words.

| k | n | i | f | e |

g

k | | | | | | g

c

w | | | | l

Circle the silent letter in each word.

Note for parent: This activity will give your child practice in recognizing and spelling words with a silent letter.

More Silent Letters

Read the story. Add the silent consonant to each of the highlighted words.

At the end of **Ras p berry** Road there

is a spooky old house. They say no one

lives there—only the **g h ost** that wails

and moans.

Thomas was going to explore. He was

wearing his "I am brave" **ba d ge**.

He walked the **len g th** of the overgrown

garden. Then he **clim b ed** the rickety stairs.

His stomach was tied in **k nots**.

"Is anyone there?"

He **k nocked** on the door. He **lis t ened**

but there was no **ans w er**...

...only the banging of a **cu _ board** door.

He **_ new** it was **dum _** to believe in

g _ osts. "I wonder what is really inside?"

Note for parent: Encourage your child to write an ending for the story. Try to include at least one word with a silent consonant.

37

Homophones

Some words sound the same but can have different meanings and spellings. They are called homophones.

Choose the correct homophone to complete each sentence.

"Come on kids," says Mom. "It's time for .... vacation!"

our
hour

Ted can't remember .... he packed his favorite toy.

weather
whether

"It's not .... ," says Tessa. "I want the window seat!"

fare
fair

Dad is looking forward to the .... from work.

brake
break

The .... goes faster and faster down the runway.

plane
plain

"I can't wait to feel the sand beneath my .... feet," says Tilly.

bear
bare

Write a sentence. Include one of the homophones you haven't used yet.

....

....

Note for parent: For added challenge, encourage your child to write a new sentence that continues the theme of the family vacation.

More Homophones

Complete the sentences by adding the correct homophones.

"It's really .... good to have a .... in your laces!"

knot
not

"Come over .... if you can't

.... what I'm saying."

hear
here

medal
meddle

"Don't .... with your brother's

swimming ...."

tail
tale

"Did I tell you the .... of how the cat lost her .... ?"

"We .... our dinner at

half past ...."

new
knew

ate
eight

"I never .... the band

had a .... song out."

great
grate

"At first, I thought it was .... , but then the music started to ...."

Homographs

Some words are spelled the same but can have different meanings. They are called homographs.

Match each homograph to the correct definition.

| bat   band   live   change   tear |

1. .... to become different

2. .... a group of musicians or singers

3. .... to have life

4. .... to pull something to pieces

5. .... a strip or loop of material

6. .... a handful of coins

7. .... something that is happening at the moment

8. .... a club of wood or metal, used to hit a ball

9. .... a drop of liquid that comes from the eye

10. .... a small mammal that flies

Say each word in a sentence.
You will notice that sometimes
homographs can be spelled
the same but have a
different sound.

Note for parent: Homographs are spelled the same but have a different meaning—and sometimes a different sound.

Making the Long u Sound

The diagraphs **ew**, **ue**, **ui**, and **ou** all make a long **u** sound as in these words:

| flew | true | fruit | you |

Circle all the words in the poem with a long **u** sound.
List the words beneath.

Take in the sights of the deep ocean blue

as you enjoy our tasty seaweed stew.

Don't be timid, just come on through,

and try the delicious squid barbeque.

You don't need a tie or a suit, it's true,

just a snorkel and flippers, you're one of the crew.

This is all brand new, it's the best value,

so come to Happy Snappers, we're waiting for you!

....

....

....

Note for parent: The long u sound (you) can be produced by adding ew and ue to the end of some words—and the letters ui and ou to others.

41

Soft c and Hard c

The letter **c** can sometimes make a soft sound like a **s**.

| cereal   face |

The letter **c** can also make a hard sound like a **k**.

| crust   cake |

Draw a circle around all the words with a soft **c** sound.
Zap all the words with a hard **c** sound.

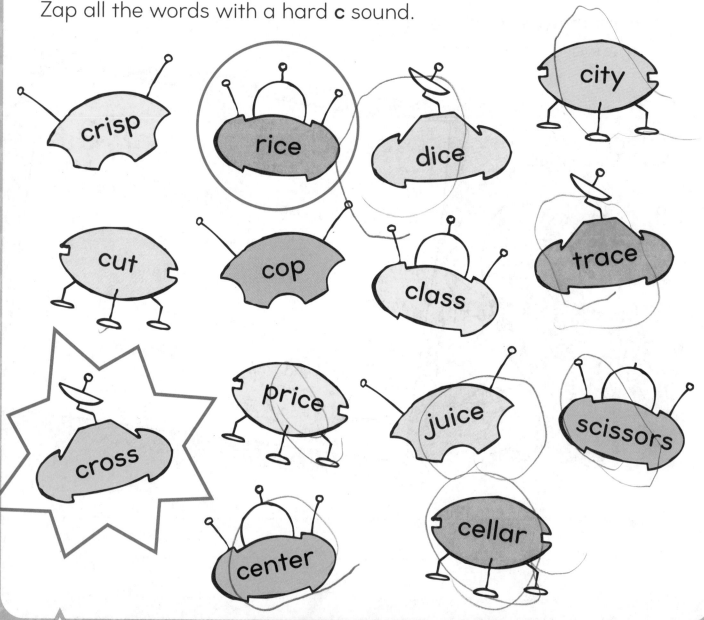

Note for parent: When the letter c appears in front of an e, i, or y it usually creates a soft s sound.

Words Starting with uni and in

Sometimes, the letters at the start of a word can help us understand its meaning.

The letters **uni** at the start of a word mean "one" or "the same."
The unicorn has one horn on its head.

The letters **in** at the start of a word can mean "into" or "not."
The doctor injected me with medicine.

Complete the words in these sentences with the prefix **uni** or **in**.

1. The ....uni....cycle is difficult to ride because it has one wheel.

2. There is only one ....uni....verse, but it contains all the stars and planets!

3. The superhero was ....in....visible, so her enemies could not see her.

4. The scientist ....in....put his commands into the robot.

5. The pilots were all wearing the same ....uni....form.

6. Linda ....in....flated the balloon by blowing air into it.

7. The team did not need Tom, so he was ....in....active.

Note for parent: Common prefixes, as well as context clues, can help your child to work out the meaning of unfamiliar words.

43

Words Starting with bi and tri

The letters **bi** at the start of a word can mean "two"—and the letters **tri** can mean "three." Add **bi** or **tri** to complete these words.

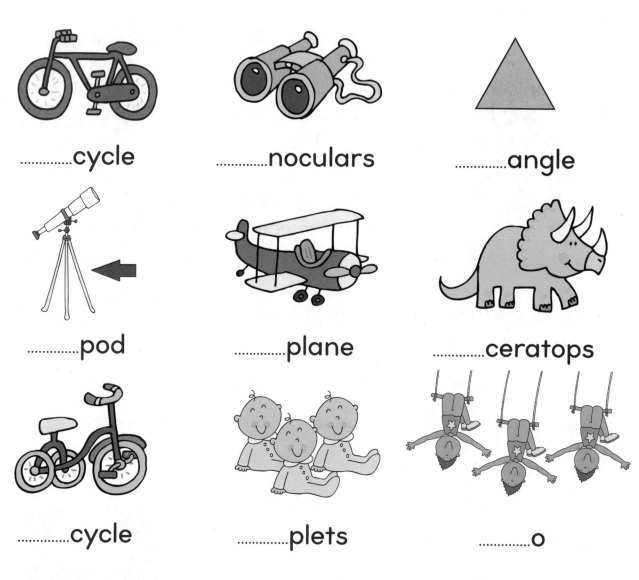

............cycle

............noculars

............angle

............pod

............plane

............ceratops

............cycle

............plets

............o

Write a sentence that includes one or more of the words that you have made.

....

....

Note for parent: The prefix bi comes from the Latin and means "two" or "twice." The prefix tri comes from the Latin meaning "three."

Compound Words

Use each word to make a compound word.

rain	....

book	....

....	ball

....	pack

Circle the compound words in each of these sentences.

1. We always use the crosswalk because the road is really busy.

2. Sophie can't fit all of her clothes in the suitcase.

3. Jackson put his auntie's hat on top of the snowman.

4. The detective uses his notebook to write down all the clues.

5. Mom was annoyed because my bedroom was a mess.

Note for parent: Compound words are mostly formed by joining two nouns together or joining an adjective or a verb to a noun.

More Compound Words

Add the missing compound words to these sentences.

playground	sandwich	baseball	seesaw
lifeguard	jellyfish	somewhere	afternoon

1. At the .... we enjoyed playing on the ....

2. Jade looked for .... to buy a ....

3. In the .... , Harry went to the .... game.

4. The .... warned us there were .... in the sea.

Write your own sentences that include a compound word.

1. ....

....

2. ....

....

Note for parent: This activity will give your child further practice in recognizing compound words and using them in their own writing.

Words with an **irl** or **url** ending share the same sound.

swirl curl

Add the correct endings (**irl** or **url**) to these words to complete the poem.

It is time for a new superhero!

When danger calls,

I will stand tall.

My arms will unf................... ,

and then I will tw................... .

Round and round,

in a fast spinning wh................... .

Oh dear, I feel sick—I'm going to h................... ,

that might be the end of ballerina g................... .

Write your own sentences about a superhero. Try and include at least one word with an **irl** or **url** ending.

.... girl is going to save the day! She will ....

....

Note for parent: Encourage your child to look back at the example words and the poem for inspiration when writing their own sentences.

47

Words with eight, aight, ait, or ate

Complete the words in these sentences using the endings **eight, aight, ait,** or **ate.**

Top secret instructions (*)

At twenty past e................, go down to the green g................ .

Cross the creaky wooden bridge (don't worry, it will hold your

w................). Then, go str................ down the path to the old fr................

train. Look inside to find the cr................ . You must rot................ the

numbers on the lock. (The code is today's d................ .)

Take what is inside, then w................ for further instructions.

And remember, don't be l................ !

(*) For your eyes only.

Sound out the words you have made.
They all have the same long **a** and **t** sound (**ate**).

Continue the story. Try to use some words that
end in **eight, aight, ait,** and **ate.**

Top-secret instructions (part 2)

....

....

Note for parent: These word endings all have the long a and t sound, as in ate. Straight is the only word in the aight word family!

Dividing Words into Syllables

Words can be divided up into their sound parts, called syllables. We can clap out the syllables as we say a word.

produce	→	pro / duce	→	2 syllables
delicious	→	de / li / cious	→	3 syllables
information	→	in / form / a / tion	→	4 syllables

Divide these words into their syllables. Draw a circle around the word in each group with the most syllables.

1. tiger   telephone   cookie   hammer

2. doctor   building   finally   calculator

3. elephant   hurricane   education   mountain

4. lesson   helicopter   garden   important

This monster talks in nonsense words!
Help him to count the syllables in each word.

pontraditious .... syllables

scrumanellywopter .... syllables

dockagilly .... syllables

trillafrilly .... syllables

frapalicious .... syllables

Note for parent: Syllables are the small sounds that make up a word. Each syllable must contain a vowel (a, e, i, o, u). Dividing words into syllables is useful when writing poetry.

Letter Patterns

Letter patterns can help us to spell similar words. These words belong to groups called word families.

eight → eighth → eighty

ice → icicles → icing

scene → scenery → scenic

Use the above words to help complete this story.

I remember the day I met Jack Frost. It was my .... birthday. I woke up and peered out of my window. Everywhere was white! It looked like the trees and grass had been dusted with .... I put on my coat and went out to play. There were .... hanging from the lampposts. I tried not to slip on the .... as I hurried down the path. I stopped to look around at the .... That is when I saw Jack Frost. He was painting .... on a tree with a big paint brush!

"Happy birthday," he smiled to me. "It's my birthday, too—I'm three hundred and .... two."

"Really?" I gasped. He looked like a boy, no older than me.

"Take my hand," he said. "Would you like a .... tour?" He lifted me up and then we were flying, high above the treetops. Everywhere was sparkling white, and the air was crisp and bright. "This is my favorite time of year," said Jack Frost. "I've been painting with .... since the age of .... Would you like to try?"

"Yes, please!" I said. "I can't wait!"

Note for parent: This activity will give your child further practice in recognizing root words and spelling patterns. Encourage them to continue the story.

Words with qu

The letters **qu** give a word the **kw** sound. Sound out these words.

| **qu**estion | **qu**art | li**qu**id | a**qu**arium |

Complete the grid by solving the clues.
Each word has the letters **qu**.

1. a shape with four equal sides
2. a female ruler of a country
3. a word that means "fast."
4. a line of people or cars
5. a coin equal to twenty-five cents
6. a noise made by a duck

1 S Q U A R E
2 Q U E E N
3 Q U I C K
4 Q U E U E
5 Q U A R T E R
6 Q U A C K

The letters in the colored squares will spell a hidden **qu** word.

....

Think of some more words that have the letters **qu**.

....

....

Words with or, er, and ar

The True News website has a few problems. Complete the word endings by using **or**, **er**, or **ar**.

TRUE NEWS

Police officer saves zoo visit**or** from hungry alligat**er**! "He was so brave," says boy.

Sail**er** loses his anch**or** overboard. The search continues...

"I bought a toast**er** for a doll**er**. Inside, I found a diamond coll**er**."

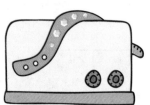

"I get my food delivered by helicopt**er**," says the famous act**er**.

Man invents sug**ar** and vineg**er** potato chips.

LATEST NEWS: "White is out!" Meet the pol__ bear who is trying out a new col__ for summer.

Note for parent: This activity will give your child practice in spelling different words that have the same er sound ending.

Spelling Challenge

Trevor the Troll needs help with his spelling. Some of these words are spelled incorrectly. Help him by circling each incorrect word.

enuff	deside	brekfast	peeple
anser	becus	nife	through
please	possibel	swimming	circul

Correctly spell each word that you have circled to help Trevor remember.

....

....

....

....

Note for parent: This activity will help your child to reinforce their learning by recognizing and correcting commonly misspelled words.

Language Arts

Helping Your Child

- The activities in this section will help your child to learn how to use nouns, pronouns, verbs, adjectives, and adverbs in sentences.

- Your child will learn how to punctuate sentences with capital letters, commas, quotation marks, and periods.

- There is practice in identifying simple and complex sentences, and how to choose appropriate words or phrases for effect.

- Set aside time to do the activities together. Do a little at a time so that your child enjoys learning.

- The answers begin on page 308.

Contents

Nouns

Nouns are words that name a person, a place, or a thing.

Ellie likes to walk her **dog** in the **park**.

person—Ellie   place—park   thing—dog

Circle the nouns in these sentences. Write out
the person, place, and thing in each sentence.

1. The (man) left his (coat) in the (restaurant.)

person ....   place ....   thing ....

2. "I need new shoes," said Max. "Can we go to the mall?"

person ....   place ....   thing ....

3. The explorer needs a map to find his way through the jungle.

person ....   place ....   thing ....

4. Jemma likes to fly her kite in the park.

person ....   place ....   thing ....

5. The astronaut went to the moon in a rocket.

person ....   place ....   thing ....

6. Mom reminded me that my packed lunch was in the kitchen.

person ....   place ....   thing ....

Make up your own sentence that has a noun for a person,
place, and thing.

....

Note for parent: Common nouns are words that represent a person, place, or thing
(such as an object or animal).

Proper Nouns

Proper nouns are words that name a **specific** person, place, or thing. We always use a capital letter for a proper noun.

Miss **Dimple's** favorite book is *The Secret Garden*.
On **Saturday**, we are going to **San Francisco** to visit **Amelia**.

Circle the proper nouns in this poem.

If I could go anywhere, then where would I choose?

Hmm, perhaps a vacation on Mars? No—maybe a Nile cruise.

On Monday, I'll climb the Great Pyramid,

Then ride on a camel. Sounds rather splendid!

On Tuesday, to London for tea with the queen,

"Oh, my dear," she'll say. "Try China, have you been?"

On Wednesday, I'll be skateboarding with Tom, my best friend,

along the Great Wall of China. It never seems to end!

On Thursday, I'll eat noodles and rice in Japan,

Then onto the Arctic to build an amazing snowman.

On Friday, to New York where my poor head is ringing,

I just shouted from the top of the Empire State Building.

On Saturday, I'll visit Gran because her cakes are too yummy,

And her little cat, Chalky, likes to sleep on my tummy.

On Sunday... OK, I think it's time for a rest,

And sometimes being home is the absolute best.

Note for parent: Proper nouns represent specific people, places, or things. Help your child to use an atlas to explore some of the locations mentioned in the poem.

57

Pronouns

A **pronoun** is a word you can use to replace a noun.
They can be singular or plural.
Singular pronouns: I, you, me, she, he, his, her, him, your, my, mine, it
Plural pronouns: we, us, they, them, our, ours, you, their

Complete these sentences by adding a pronoun.

1. The witch was excited because ...*she*.......... new broomstick had just arrived.

2. Jade was confident ....*He*........ could swim across the lake.

3. "The toy is broken. ......*It*......... can't be fixed."

4. "I'm going to the park, Sam. Do ....*You*..... want to come with ......*me*......?"

5. The ugly sisters were happy, because ....*thtf*..... were invited to the ball.

6. "I've lost my keys," said Dad. "Have you seen ....*it*...?"

7. "Hey, that coat belongs to me," said Sarah. "It's ....*Hers*..!"

8. Ben and Chris love to make milkshakes. Banana and strawberry are
...*thir*............ favorite flavors.

Abstract Nouns

A **noun** is something we can see, touch, taste, hear, and smell— like a person, place, or thing.

An abstract noun is something you can't see, touch, taste, hear, and smell. Here are some examples of abstract nouns.

jealousy

honesty

trust

kindness

anger

bravery

love

Circle the abstract nouns in these sentences.

1. To cure his boredom, the god Zeus made Pandora.

2. Pandora had great beauty.

3. She fell in love with a man called Epimetheus.

4. He showed kindness and bravery.

5. Zeus was filled with jealousy and decided to trick them.

6. He gave them a box and said, "If you open this, you will break my trust."

7. Pandora's curiosity led her to open the box.

8. Out flew all the ills of the world, including sorrow and anger.

9. But at the bottom of the box was a tiny hope.

10. "Do not be upset. I will bring happiness to the world," it said.

Note for parent: Abstract nouns are things that we can't interact with using the five senses. They usually represent a quality, an emotion, or a feeling.

59

Verms

A **verb** is a word that describes what someone or something does.

Choose a verb from the box to complete each sentence.

swim	climb	run	bake	write	scream

1. The scary movie made me ....!

2. Amira likes to .... to her pen pal in Australia.

3. Because we were late, we had to .... for the school bus.

4. Ali had to .... over the rocks to reach the cave.

Choose the correct form of the verb in each sentence.

1. The cars (drive/drives) slowly through the thick fog.

2. The magician (produces/produce) a rabbit out of a hat.

3. The tree branches (wave/waves) back and forth in the wind.

4. Noah (practices/practice) his piano for one hour every night.

5. The captain (chooses/choose) the best players for his team.

Write two sentences of your own using a verb in each sentence.

....

....

....

....

Helping Verbs

A **helping verb** is always used before a main verb.
They help the main verb to make sense in a sentence.

We **were** looking for the lost cat.
I wish I **could** remember where I left my bag.
My brother **was** wearing his new coat.
She **would** like another piece of cake.

Choose a helping verb from the box to complete each sentence.

is   am   are   have   has   will   was   were   had   can   could   would

1. I wish I .... looked at the map before leaving home.

2. We .... try the mushroom pizza for a change.

3. "Look, the monkey .... swinging in the tree!"

4. I .... singing in the talent contest tomorrow.

5. Yesterday, the girls .... baking cookies.

6. Last night, my dad .... fixing my broken toy.

Write two sentences of your own using a helping verb and a main verb.

....

....

....

Note for parent: Helping verbs help the main verb to make sense. They also give more detail about when a sentence is taking place. For example, in the past or the present.

61

Adjectives

An **adjective** describes a noun.

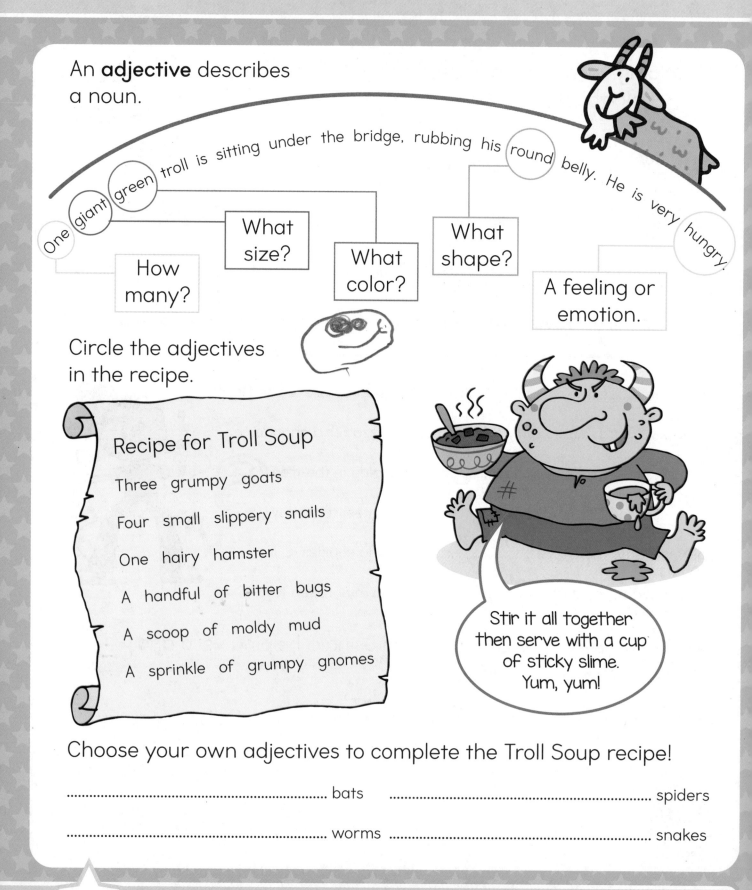

One giant green troll is sitting under the bridge, rubbing his round belly. He is very hungry.

How many?

What size?

What color?

What shape?

A feeling or emotion.

Circle the adjectives in the recipe.

Recipe for Troll Soup

Three grumpy goats

Four small slippery snails

One hairy hamster

A handful of bitter bugs

A scoop of moldy mud

A sprinkle of grumpy gnomes

Stir it all together then serve with a cup of sticky slime. Yum, yum!

Choose your own adjectives to complete the Troll Soup recipe!

.... bats .... spiders

.... worms .... snakes

Adverbs

An **adverb** is a word that describes a verb.
They can describe...

How an action happens.   →   The boy ran **quickly** to catch the ball.

When an action happens.   →   **Tomorrow**, we are going on vacation.

Where an action happens.   →   Kelly plays basketball **outside**.

How often an action happens. →   I walk my dog **every** day.

Circle the adverb in each sentence and underline the verb it is describing.

1. Sometimes we have to share with others.

2. The goat trotted nervously across the troll's bridge.

3. Sam was jumping excitedly up and down.

4. Debbie waited quietly in the lunch line.

5. The crowd cheered loudly when the player scored.

Choose your own adverb to complete each sentence.

1. I .... hand my homework in on time.

2. Mom sang .... to the baby.

3. .... , we watched the football game.

4. He .... gave me some of his candy.

Note for parent: An adverb can describe how, when, where, and how often an action happens. For example, slowly, carefully, before, after, inside, outside, always, never.

Regular and Irregular Plural Nouns

To make a **regular** plural we just add **s** to the end of a noun.

car ➔ car**s**   book ➔ book**s**   pear ➔ pear**s**

Not all nouns follow that rule.
These are called **irregular** plural nouns.

If a noun ends in a **consonant** and a **y**, we add **ies**.

baby ➔ bab**ies**   story ➔ stor**ies**   city ➔ cit**ies**

If a noun ends in **s**, **ch**, **ss**, **x** or **z**, we add **es**.

box ➔ box**es**   bus ➔ bus**es**   dish ➔ dish**es**

If a noun ends in **f** or **fe**, we change the f to a **v** and add **es**.

knife ➔ kni**ves**   leaf ➔ lea**ves**   wolf ➔ wol**ves**

Write the plural for each word.

glass	....	country	....
quiz	....	scarf	....
boat	....	fox	....
puppy	....	shelf	....
brush	....	phone	....
wife	....	day	....

Note for parent: Provide further practice by listing words for your child to pluralize.

More Irregular Plural Nouns

Some irregular plural nouns don't seem to follow any rules!

goose → geese   man → men

deer → deer   ox → oxen

Look for the irregular plurals of these words in the letter grid.

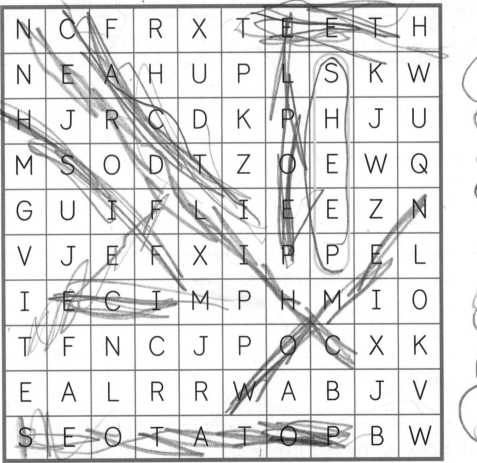

N	C	F	R	X	T	E	E	T	H	H
N	E	A	H	U	P	L	S	K	W
H	J	R	C	D	K	P	H	J	U
M	S	O	D	T	Z	O	E	W	Q
G	U	I	F	L	I	E	E	Z	N
V	J	E	F	X	I	P	P	E	L
I	E	C	I	M	P	H	M	I	O
T	F	N	C	J	P	O	C	X	K
E	A	L	R	R	W	A	B	J	V
S	E	O	T	A	T	O	P	B	W

sheep
child
cactus
tooth
foot
mouse
potato
fish
woman
person

Write the irregular plurals you have found below.

sheep

....

....

Note for parent: Some plural nouns don't follow any of the regular rules for making plurals. With practice your child will become familiar with their spelling.

65

Past, Present, and Future

Past tense	Present tense	Future tense
(add **d** or **ed**)		(add **will** + **verb**)
I walk**ed**	I walk	I **will walk**
I exercis**ed**	I exercise	I **will exercise**

Complete the table.

past	present	future
The crowd cheered	cheers	they will
danced	She dances	will dancers
she is gom	she opened	We will open
Climed	Charlie climbs	Will clime
The dog barked		

Rewrite these sentences in the past tense.

1. We will learn how to ride a bike safely.

We learnt howton

2. I enjoy playing basketball with my friends.

....

Rewrite these sentences in the future tense.

1. The teacher called out our names in class.

....

2. We decorate the cake with chocolate icing.

....

Note for parent: To change a verb to the past tense, we can usually add d or ed to it. For the future tense, we can add the word "will" before the verb.

Spelling in the Past Tense

Sometimes when a verb changes to the past tense, the spelling of the verb can change.

Past tense	Present tense	Future tense
I **went**	I go	I will go
We **ran**	We run	We will run
She **ate**	She eats	She will eat
I **spoke**	I speak	I will speak

Change the verb in brackets to the correct past-tense spelling of the verb.

1. We (tell) .... *told* .... stories and (sing) .... *sang* .... songs around the campfire.

2. Leo (write) .... *wrote* .... his name on the front of his notepad.

3. I (ring) .... *rang* .... the school bell at the end of breaktime.

4. The cat (is) .... *was* .... chasing the mouse.

5. Sam (buy) .... *bought* .... a strawberry milkshake and a hamburger.

6. Mom (hang) .... *hung* .... my painting on the bedroom wall.

7. I jumped and (catch) .... *caught* .... the ball!

8. They (are) .... *were* .... hoping to arrive on time, but the

concert had already (begin) .... *began* ....

Write about what you did yesterday. Circle all the past-tense verbs.

.... i *forgot* wut i did yesterday ....

....

Note for parent: Some verbs have an alternate spelling when they change to the past tense. For example: drink/drank, catch/caught, make/made, and so on.

67

Verb and Pronoun Agreement

If the pronoun is **he**, **she**, or **it**, then we add **s** to most verbs in the present tense.

| He walk**s** | She wait**s** | It jump**s** |

If the pronoun is **I**, **we**, **you**, and **they**, then we do not change most verbs in the present tense.

| I dance | You dance | They dance | We dance |

If there is a noun or a proper noun before the verb, then we also add **s** in the present tense.

| Tom climb**s** | The girl talk**s** | The dog play**s** |

Circle the correct verbs in the following story.

I (sit/sits) and (waits/wait) nervously outside the principal's office. Jessica (walk/walks) past me and (stick/sticks) out her tongue.

"In trouble again?" she (asks/ask).

I (shrugs/shrug) my shoulders. "Who cares? I'm always in trouble."

She (laugh/laughs) and (skip/skips) off down the corridor. Then I (hears/hear) the door open. I (stands/stand) up. The principal (wave/waves) me inside.

"Well," he (say/says), "I understand you have been telling your teacher some tall tales again." He (tap/taps) his fingers on the table.

"It's the truth, honest!" I (say/says).

"Hmm, I think we might (disagree/disagrees). Like the time you told her a rocket ship landed in your garden. And that made you late for class." He (shakes/shake) his head.

"It did, sir." I (lower/lowers) my eyes to the floor. "She never (believes/believe) me."

"And this time?" the principal (ask/asks).

I (clear/clears) my throat. "Sir, it's the truth. An elephant really did eat my homework!"

Note for parent: A present-tense prerb must agree with its pronoun. Encourage your child to continue the story in the present tense.

Capital Letters and Periods

All sentences must start with a capital letter. We can end a sentence with a period mark.

the ball is red   The ball is red.

we went to the movies   We went to the movies.

If we didn't do this, then sentences would be very confusing! Read the following diary entry, circle letters that should be capitals, and add period marks to make complete sentences.

Sunday

we went to the beach i bought a yummy strawberry ice cream i had to eat it quickly because it was melting in the sun mom and dad went swimming but I decided to go exploring i found a rock pool and there was a big shiny shell in the water when I went to pick it up it started to move there was a hermit crab living inside and the shell was its home i picked up some other shells and gave them to my sister to put on her sandcastle

Note for parent: All complete sentences start with a capital letter and end with a punctuation mark. This can be a period, an exclamation mark, or a question mark.

69

Capitalization and Punctuation

You can be the teacher now! The story is missing some capital letters, periods, and question marks. Help the writer correct their mistakes and complete the sentences.

T
the tale of the missing Bananas

the monkey was angry. he was beating his chest and

jumping up and down   Someone had stolen all his bananas

"it's not fair," he said

all the animals gathered around

"are you sure you didn't eat them " asked the zebra

the monkey shook his head

"when did you last see them " squawked the parrot

The monkey scratched his chin

"my large eyes might help me find them," said the owl

Suddenly, there was a loud bang   Everyone turned to see

what had happened   the elephant was lying on his back

His legs were kicking in the air

"i slipped on a banana peel!" the elephant grumbled

"Look, there's more of them and they lead into the jungle,"

said the owl

"come on," said the monkey. "let's follow the trail "

Writing Sentences

A trail of banana peels has led the animals into the jungle. See the previous page for the beginning of the story.

Continue the story. Remember to begin your sentences with a capital letter, then decide how to end your sentence—with a period, an exclamation mark, or a question mark. Use lots of verbs, adjectives, and adverbs, too.

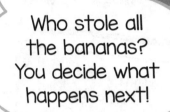

Who stole all the bananas? You decide what happens next!

Note for parent: Encourage your child to continue the story and to check their sentences for capital letters and punctuation marks.

71

Book and Movie Titles

Capitalize	Don't capitalize
First letter of the title All nouns and verbs	a, an, and, at, but, from, if, is, of, on, or, the, to

Capitalize these book titles.

1 when dinosaurs attack!

2 escape from wizard mountain

3 the owls of the forest

1. ....

2. ....

3. ....

Add the titles to these movie posters:

my neighbor is a zombie!

robo captain saves the day

Note for parent: Conjunctions (and, but, or), articles (the, an, a), and prepositions (of, at, to) are not capitalized unless they are the first word in the title.

More Proper Nouns

Find and correct eight missing capital letters for proper nouns in this text. The first one is done for you.

U
~~U~~luru, also known as ayer's rock, is a large sandstone rock formation in australia.

Uluru is very important to the Aboriginal people of australia because they believe

it was created by their ancestor spirits.

The rock stands more than 1,000 feet above sea level (that's higher than the

eiffel tower in france!) and can be seen for many miles around.

At the bottom of uluru, there are caves with

rock paintings as well as lots of bats!

Note for parent: Help your child to find out further facts about Uluru in Australia and encourage them to write their own sentences about what they have learned.

73

Conjunctions

Conjunctions are connecting words. Like a jigsaw piece, they help us to join two sentences together.

| Luke went to the mall. | He bought a new T-shirt. |

Luke went to the mall, **and** he bought a new T-shirt.

When we make a conjunction, we also add a comma before the conjunction.

Combine each pair of sentences using one of the conjunctions below. Rewrite the sentence underneath.

and   but   yet   when   so

I. The bus never came. We took a taxi instead.

....

2. It was cloudy and foggy. We still went to the park.

....

3. I was just about to fall asleep. I heard a loud bang.

....

4. Yasin wants to buy a new game. He can't decide which one.

....

5. Hannah threw the ball. Her dog chased after it.

....

Complex Sentences

Sometimes a sentence can have two or more parts.

| Toby made a sandwich | because he was hungry. |

Draw a line to link the first part of each sentence to the correct second part.

| | we are going to get pizza. |

| Although it was raining, | while the teacher waited. |

| | we went out for a walk. |

| Charlotte couldn't finish the puzzle | Joe spotted a few mistakes. |

| After we watch the movie, | |

| | because a piece was missing. |

| I quickly looked for my school bag, | |

| | he gave a loud roar! |

| While he was checking his spelling, | |

| When the lion woke up, | |

Note for parent: Sentences are made up of clauses (parts). A main clause makes sense on its own (Toby made a sandwich) and a dependent clause gives additional information.

Moving Parts of a Sentence

We can swap the order of a sentence.

| When he leaves school, | Tom wants to go to college. |

Tom wants to go to college when he leaves school.

Write each sentence again, by swapping the order around.

| If Mom can find her keys, | we can drive to the water park. |

We can drive to the water park if Mom can find her keys.

| Later that day, | I heard the news. |

....

| Unless you have a ticket, | you can't enter the stadium. |

....

| Because he was tired, | Luke went to bed. |

....

| While I ate a hot dog, | I watched the football game. |

....

Note for parent: If the main clause begins the sentence, there is no need for a comma to divide the clauses.

More Complex Sentences

Complex sentences may have more than one part (or clause). Read the following sentence:

When we go camping, we have to make sure we pack the insect spray because there will be lots of bugs around.

There are three parts in this sentence.

Circle the three parts in each of these sentences.

1. As soon as it stops raining, I am going to go out and play because I need some fresh air.

2. Unless Mila gets her allowance, she cannot buy the new dress because she doesn't have enough money.

3. Although he was very tired, Yasin could not sleep while the storm was raging.

4. When Emily saw the Spooky Forest Maze, she decided she could not go in unless someone else went with her.

Note for parent: Look at sentences your child has written throughout this book and identify the parts (or clauses) in each one.

77

Commas in Addresses

When we write an address on an envelope, we put a comma between the city and the state zip code.

Henry Moore
56 Greenfield Drive
Houston, TX 77019

When we write an address in a sentence, we add commas to separate the street address, city, and state:

Henry Moore lives at 56 Greenfield Drive, Houston, TX 77019.

Write these addresses on the envelopes.

Talisa Mitchell lives at 68 Pearl Gardens, Miami, FL 33145.

Kadeem Nelson lives at 11 Rosewater Falls, Chicago, IL 60034.

Write your address on this envelope.

....

....

....

Then write your address in a sentence.

I live at ....

....

....

Note for parent: Help your child to find the addresses of family and friends, and write these in sentences and for an envelope.

Writing a List

Commas separate items in a list.

Dad went shopping and bought apples (,) milk (,) bread (,) orange juice (,) and potatoes.

Take out the extra "ands" in these sentences and replace them with commas.

1. Inside the chest was a bag of gold and a sparkling gem and a rusty key and an old map.

....

....

2. I put the pencil and the eraser and the crayons and the ruler back into my pencil case.

....

....

You can use a **colon** to start a list if the list comes after a complete sentence.

The ice cream comes in three different flavors (:) strawberry, chocolate, and cherry.

Complete this list by describing the items in the suitcase. Then add three more items of your own. Don't forget to start your list with a colon.

Mason had packed lots of things for his vacation:

....

....

....

Note for parent: Commas follow each item in a list. If the list follows a complete sentence/main clause, then a colon is used to introduce the list.

79

Quotation Marks

Quotation marks ("........") are drawn around the words that are spoken in a sentence.

Goldilocks said, "This porridge is too salty."

| We put a comma before the first quotation mark. | The first word is always capitalized. | Any punctuation comes before the last quotation mark. |

Correct these sentences, adding in the quotation marks and a period, or an exclamation mark.

1. Gretel gasped,   The cottage is made of candy

2. The wolf growled,   All the better to see you with

3. Jack said,   I am going to plant the magic beans

4. Cinderella cried,   I must be home before midnight

5. The dwarf laughed,   Our home has never been

so tidy.

Commas and Quotation Marks

Sometimes we want to split up a line of speech.

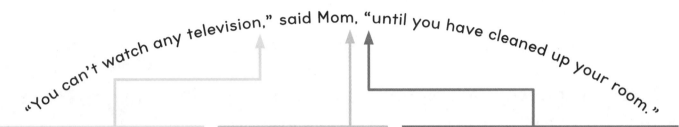

"You can't watch any television," said Mom, "until you have cleaned up your room."

| The comma comes before the quotation mark. | This comma tells us that the sentence continues. | We don't use a capital letter here because we are continuing the sentence. |

Correct these sentences, adding in the quotation marks and the correct punctuation to end the sentence.

1.   If you believe,   said Peter,   then you will be able to fly

2.   By sticking to the path,   said Wendy,   we can't get lost

3.   They are only kids,   grumbled the pirate,   so they can't beat us

4.   I might be small,   the fairy giggled,   but I'm still smarter than you are

5.   Don't get too close,   warned the mermaid,   or else I'll

splash you with my tail

Note for parent: Remind your child to refer to the rules at the top of the page when checking their sentences.

Direct and Indirect Speech

Direct speech uses quotation marks and tells us exactly what is said.

"The treasure is buried beside the palm tree," said the pirate.

Indirect speech is telling someone what was said.

The pirate said the treasure was buried beside the palm tree.

Change these sentences to **indirect** speech.

"If I get a kiss, then I will become a prince," said the frog.

The frog said ....

"I will make myself wings and fly like a bird," boasted Icarus.

Icarus boasted ....

"Good thoughts are as bright as sunbeams," said the fairy.

The fairy said ....

Change these sentences to **direct** speech.

Scarlet told everyone her grandma was a wolf!

"Grandma is ....

The Genie explained Aladdin had three wishes.

"You have ....

The hare teased the tortoise, saying he was too slow.

"You are ....

Note for parent: Direct speech is when the exact spoken words are given in quotation marks. Indirect speech reports what was said, usually in the past tense.

Adding Quotation Marks

Add the missing quotation marks to this story around the words that are spoken. The first two are done for you.

"Your puny life is over, Human," said the alien. And your spaceship is now mine!

Actually, it's my mom's ship, said Kid Phoenix. I can't give you what is hers.

Are you questioning me? squealed the alien. What is hers is now mine!

I don't think so, laughed Phoenix. Besides, our plan is much better than yours.

Hardly. My space fleet has its blasters aimed at your planet, sneered the alien.

And our candy cannon just turned yours into marshmallow, grinned Phoenix. So, eat that, alien!

Note for parent: Encourage your child to continue the story on a separate piece of paper, making correct use of quotation marks for direct speech.

83

Singular Possessive Nouns

An apostrophe **s** can be used to show that one thing belongs to something else.

The woman**'s** hat blew away in the wind.

The **'s** tells us that the hat belongs to the woman.

Rewrite the part of each sentence that is underlined by adding 's to the possessive noun.

1. The ball of Luke went over the wall.

   Luke's ball went over the wall.
   ....

2. The ball smashed the window of Mrs. Baker.

   ....

3. She screamed and woke up the dog of her neighbor.

   ....

4. The dog went barking into the garden of Mr. Nelson.

   ....

5. His cat gave a screech and jumped into the tree of Miss Clemons.

   ....

6. "What is all this racket?" complained the mom of Luke.

   ....

Nothing to do with me! Honest!

Note for parent: This activity will give your child opportunity to review and practice using singular possessive nouns.

Plural Possessive Nouns

If the plural possessive noun ends in an **s**, then we add an apostrophe after the **s**.

The boys' bicycles were all muddy.

If the plural possessive noun ends in a different letter, then we add an apostrophe, and an **s**.

The children's toys were broken.

Turn each of the nouns in brackets into a plural possessive noun.

I. Alice was looking for the (girl)..........girls'.............. changing room.

2. The (woman)................................. tennis club was recruiting new members.

3. My (parent)................................. car was parked on the drive.

4. The magazine won the (People)................................. Top Choice Award.

5. It was hard work cleaning out the (animal)................................. cages.

6. The (teacher)................................. staff room is out of bounds.

7. Next month, the (waiter)................................. uniforms are changing.

8. The (baby)................................. strollers were lined up in a row.

Note for parent: Remind your child of the rules regarding plural possessive nouns when checking their work.

85

Contractions

Poor Cinderella. Her stepsisters are being mean to her again! Change these contractions from spoken language (can't, won't, we'll) to written language (cannot, will not, we will).

You **won't** go to the ball .... will not ....

We **couldn't** be seen with such a scruffy girl ....

You **don't** even have a dress. ....

It's no good, your hair is a mess! ....

We **wouldn't** want to be unkind, ...

But the prince **doesn't** like you – he's not blind! ....

Wait, your foot **shouldn't** fit inside that shoe... ....

We **can't** believe it. He did choose you! ....

Note for parent: A contraction is a shortened form of two words. This activity will give your child practice in identifying and spelling contractions.

More Contractions

Complete the story sentences by adding the correct contractions.

Han and Hilda were very poor.

"We (do not) .... have any food," said Han.

"(It is) .... true," sighed Hilda. "(There is) .... nothing left!"

The next day, Han was walking through the woods. His stomach was rumbling because

he was very hungry. "Where will I find something to eat?" he wondered. All of a

sudden, he heard a sound. It was louder than his rumbling belly!

It was a high-pitched squeaking. Suspicious of what it might be,

he stepped off the path to investigate.

To his surprise, there was a fairy—and she was caught in

a thorny bush. Carefully, Han freed the fairy.

"I (cannot) .... believe it, you saved my life!"

giggled the fairy. "Please let me grant you a wish."

Han gave a big smile. "A wish? Gosh, (it is) .... my lucky day! I know

I need to think about this carefully. I (would not) .... want to waste it!"

What do you suspect Han wishes for? Write the next paragraph in the story. Try to include two or more contractions, and a word you need to look up in a dictionary.

....

....

....

Note for parent: This activity will give your child further practice in spelling common contractions in sentences.

Formal and Informal Language

When we speak or write to people we know well, such as our family and friends, often we use informal or casual language.

"Hey, didn't mean to be late."

But if we speak or write to someone we know less well, such as a teacher, we use formal language.

"I'm very sorry. I didn't mean to be late."

Rewrite these sentences using formal language.

> Traffic is crazy. Gonna miss first class.

> Bella's not coming on trip. So sad!

....

....

....

> Would be cool to have a sleepover at my place.

> Whatcha doing next Sat?

....

....

....

Note for parent: Formal language is often used when we write. However, there are times when we might use informal language. For example, when texting or sending emails to friends.

Prefix Opposites

Choose the correct word from the box to complete each of these sentences.

disagreeable	agreeable	spell	misspell
well	unwell	possible	impossible

1. To win the game, Hannah had to .... a ten-letter word.

2. "If we hurry then I'm sure it's .... to arrive on time."

3. Lucy stayed in bed because she was feeling ....

4. Serena had some .... things to say about my baking!

5. "It's nice to see you looking so .... ," said Grandma.

6. Because of the thick fog, it was .... to see anything.

7. After thinking it over, Liam was finally .... to the plan.

8. "I'll let you write the postcard," said Sam. "I always .... the address."

Choose a prefix to add to these words to turn them into their opposite.

__lock   ___own

__polite   ___step

Note for parent: This activity will give your child further practice in recognizing how a prefix can change the meaning of a word.

89

More Practice with Suffixes

Often when we add a suffix to a base word, the spelling of the base word changes.

| swim | **ing** | swimming | happy | **ily** | happily |
| fame | **ous** | famous | loaf | **es** | loaves |

Sometimes, a suffix can also change the meaning of the base word.

| use | use**ful** | use**less** | hope | hope**ful** | hope**less** |

Add the correct suffix to the bracketed word to complete the sentences.

At one time, people thought it was (hope) ....

to try and travel to the moon. But in 1969, after a lot of

(plan) .... a mission to the moon was

(final) .... going to happen. This was NASA's

(big) .... project and everyone was very

(nerve) .... but (excite) ....

Millions of people around the world tuned in to watch

the launch and offer their (encourage) ....

to the three (courage) .... astronauts.

The launch was (success) ....

After three days of space travel, the astronauts (arrive) .... at the moon. Two of the astronauts (travel) .... down to the moon's surface in a lunar module. They (explore) .... and (collect) .... rock samples. They also (proud) .... (plant) .... the American flag on the moon to show that they had been there.

When they (return) .... home there was a lot of (happy) .... and (rejoice) .... because the mission had been a success!

Finding Words in a Dictionary

A dictionary lists words in alphabetical order. Each page of a dictionary has a guide word in each corner. They can help you to quickly find the word you are looking for.

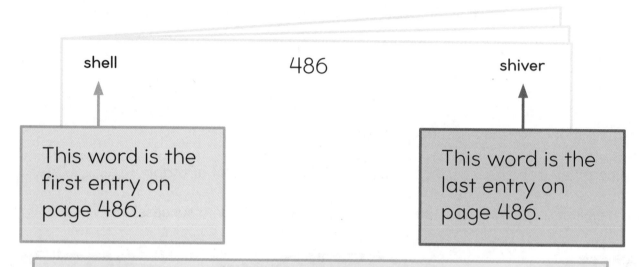

shell   486   shiver

This word is the first entry on page 486.

This word is the last entry on page 486.

You would find the words **shelter** and **ship** on this page because they come between shell and shiver.

Write down the page where you would find these words.

test	500	thin

thing	501	thought

thoughtful	502	through

throw	503	thunder

thumb ☐   thread ☐

thorn ☐   thirsty ☐

thrilling ☐   thank ☐

text ☐   thief ☐

think ☐   thud ☐

Note for parent: Remind your child that sometimes they need to look at the second, third, or fourth letter of a word (and so on) to decide its order.

Dictionary Definitions

A dictionary can explain the meaning of a word. This is known as its definition.

> **morph** *[verb]*—to change or transform into something different

Draw a line to match each of these words to its definition. Look in a dictionary to check your answers.

hurricane	a stringed instrument
catapult	a large extinct elephant
comet	a machine used to throw objects
summit	a clever tool or device
zither	a violent storm with heavy wind and rain
inhabit	an object in space made of dust and gas
gadget	to live in a place (house, town)
mammoth	the highest part of something

Find these words in a dictionary. Write a short definition for each of the words.

population ....

deciduous ....

omnivore ....

Note for parent: Remind your child that if they come across a word they do not understand, they can use a dictionary to look up its meaning.

93

Reading Unfamiliar Words

Look for clues in these sentences to help work out the meaning of the highlighted words. Circle each choice. You can use a dictionary to check your answers.

1. Everyone **concurred** that Grandpa's cake was delicious.

argued   agreed   disagreed

2. When it came to strength, the mighty warrior was **unrivaled**.

best   last   unhappy

3. The team needed a good **strategy** or else they would lose the game.

talk   rest   plan

4. I was shaking with **trepidation** as I entered the dragon's cave.

wonder   fear   sadness

5. The wizard was **incensed** because someone had stolen his favorite spell book.

hot   angry   worried

Note for parent: Look at other words within a sentence that can offer clues to the meaning of an unfamiliar word.

Improving Writing

Try to improve this story by changing the words in parentheses into more interesting or more descriptive words. Some have been done already to show you how.

Angel and Sam were (moving) ....**swimming**.... across the coral reef.

Angel said to Sam, "I'm the (best) ....~~fastest~~.... swimmer ever."

"No, you aren't!" (said) ....**argued**.... Sam. "Want to race?"

Both fish (moved) ....went.... between the bright

(green) ....**emerald**.... seaweed and the (red) ....apple.... coral.

"I'm going to win!" (said) ....~~said~~ screamed.... Angel.

"No, I am!" (said) ....I could.... Sam.

Then, all of a sudden, something (big) ....large.... (came)

....~~something~~ swam out.... out from behind a rock. It opened its jaws wide to reveal

(a lot) ....so much.... of (very big) ....bigger.... teeth!

"Shark!" (said) ....screamed.... Angel. "Quick, hide!"

The two fish (went) ....swam.... toward the nearest rocks.

When they reached the rocks, they found a small (hole) ....bump....

to hide in.

The shark was (upset) ....fricry.... because it couldn't get to them.

So the shark (went) ....swam.... away.

"We did it!" Angel (said) ....says.... "Let's call that one a draw!"

Note for parent: Words to replace "said" might include replied, responded, cried, shouted, called, etc. Your child might find it helpful to use a dictionary or thesaurus.

Adjectives with the Suffix er

We can add the suffix **er** to an adjective to compare one item with another item.

The mouse is small.

The ladybug is **smaller** than the mouse.

Choose the correct adjective from the box to complete these sentences.

taller	louder	warmer	better	slower	healthier

1. The drum is .... than the triangle.

2. I am a .... swimmer than Jack.

3. Apples are .... than cookies.

4. The tortoise was .... than the hare.

5. A skyscraper is .... than a house.

6. Summer is .... than winter.

Write a sentence using one of these adjectives to compare two items.

stronger	softer	wiser	faster	higher

....

....

Note for parent: Comparative adjectives compare one noun with another noun. They are used when only two items are being compared.

Adjectives with the Suffix est

We can add the suffix **est** to an adjective to compare one item with a group of similar items.

The Sahara Desert in Africa is the world's

largest hot desert.

Choose the correct adjectives from the box to complete these sentences.

coldest   warmest   heaviest   longest   brightest   fastest

1. Sirius (or the Dog Star) is the .... star in the night sky.

2. Antarctica is the .... place on Earth.

3. The Nile River in Egypt is the .... river in the world.

4. The .... land mammal is the African

bush elephant.

Find out the answers to these questions using books or the Internet.

What is the highest mountain in the world?

....

What is the biggest lake in the United States?

....

Note for parent: Superlative adjectives are used to compare one noun with a group of nouns in a similar category. The comparison is taken to the highest degree (heaviest, tallest, etc.).

97

Silly Sayings

Sometimes a saying can be silly and not make sense—but we know what it means.

You let the cat out of the bag.	→	you revealed a secret
Can you give me a hand?	→	I need some help
The test was a piece of cake.	→	the test was very easy

Draw a picture to illustrate each of these silly sayings.

It's raining cats and dogs.	I'm on top of the world.	It's a tempest in a teacup.

I'm all ears.	I've got cold feet.	I'm getting in shape.

Note for parent: A word or phrase that means something different from its literal or real meaning is called an idiom.

Odd One Out

Circle the word that doesn't belong with each picture.

dirty

muddy

grimy

spotless

warm

hot

frosty

burning

build

make

construct

break

nervous

timid

relaxed

afraid

Write some words that have the same meaning as those in the bubbles. Use a dictionary or thesaurus to see if you can add more.

(loud)   thunderous
....

(friend)
....

Onomatopoeia

Sometimes, the sound of a word is similar to the sound it describes. These words are called **onomatopoeia** (*ah-nuh-ma-tuh-pee-uh*).

buzz

crack   screech

whack

clang

boom

splash

hiss

pop

boing

creak

squelch

splat   bang

whoosh   crackle

fizz

vroom   squeak

Write three sentences using onomatopoeia in each sentence. You can choose from the words on this page, if you prefer, or use other onomatopoeic words you know.

....

....

....

Note for parent: Onomatopoeia is using words to describe a sound. These words sound like the object or action they describe.

More Onomatopoeia

Read these sentences that describe an action. Then write a word to describe the sound you might hear from the action.

Boing!

1. The girl was jumping on the trampoline.

boing

2. The explorer waded through the thick mud.

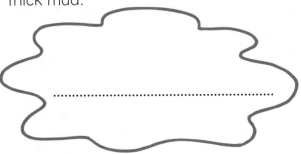

3. The race car skidded around the corner.

4. Penny shook the can of pop, then opened it!

5. I pushed on the old rusty gate.

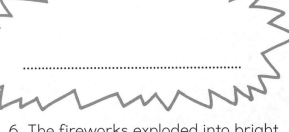

6. The fireworks exploded into bright colors.

Note for parent: This activity will give your child practice in writing words that describe familiar and imagined sounds.

101

Opposites

Complete each of the sentences by writing an opposite for the **bold** word. Little Brown Bear and Goldilocks don't seem to have a lot in common!

"This porridge is too **hot** for me!"

"It's far too .... , just like the tea."

"The bed is too **big**, don't you agree?"

"No, it's too ...., can't you see?"

"Ouch! This chair is too **hard** and creaky."

"Really? I find it too .... and squeaky!"

"I sleep with the light **on** by my bed."

"Oh, switch it .... It hurts my head."

"Why don't you ever **agree** with me?"

"Because it's more fun to ....!"

Note for parent: Your child could check their answers using a thesaurus or dictionary.

Alliteration

Sometimes we write phrases or sentences using words that have the same beginning sound. This makes our words more memorable or fun for the reader.

Seven salty sailors are singing on a ship.

Welcome to **Donut Dream Designs.**

We need your help to create some crazy new donut toppings. But they must start with the same sound!

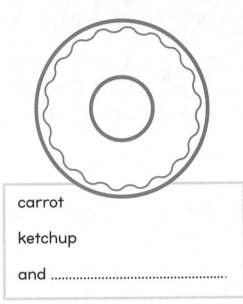

carrot

ketchup

and ....

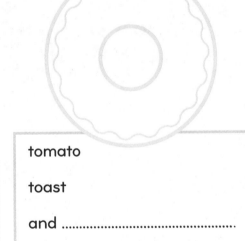

tomato

toast

and ....

Don't forget to decorate your donuts!

pizza

peanuts

and ....

mint

marmalade

and ....

Note for parent: Alliteration is when we repeat an emphasized sound in a group of words. They don't always have to start with the same letter, for example, "kite" and "crunch."

103

Reading, Comprehension, and Writing

Helping Your Child

- The activities in this section will encourage your child to learn to read for meaning, and to use ideas from reading to develop their writing skills.

- A variety of fiction and nonfiction texts are introduced including stories from around the world, classic myths, poetry, science, and geography texts.

- Your child will learn how to plan and write their own stories, poems, opinion pieces, and factual reports.

- Set aside time to do the activities together. Do a little at a time, so that your child enjoys learning.

- The answers begin on page 311.

Contents

Maushop, the Good Giant

A Legend of the Wampanoag Tribe

A long time ago, there lived a kind giant named Maushop. He was strong and courageous, and a skilled hunter. His long beard was stone gray and his eyes were as brown as the earth.

One day he met the people of the Wampanoag tribe. They invited the giant to stay with them.

"Please, good giant," they said. "Can you improve our homes?"

He saw that they were living in flimsy tepees that gave little protection from the cold and the wild beasts. So Maushop went into the grassy plains and hunted deer and bison. He used their skins to craft better homes for the people. They were very grateful, but as snow began to fall, they realized it would be a bitter winter.

"Please, good giant, make us a fire," the people asked.

Maushop went into the forest and used his tremendous strength to pull up the trees. He then chopped the wood with his magical axe and made an enormous bonfire, so the people could be warm again.

But they were still not content.

"Please, good giant, we need meat for our winter stores."

Maushop was tired from all his labors, but he agreed to help them once again.

Describe Maushop using words from the story.

....

....

Note for parent: Help your child to pronounce the difficult words in the titles above: Wampanoag (waam-puh-now-ag) and Maushop (maw-shop).

Maushop waded out into the sea and battled with the largest whale he could find. He dragged it onto the shore. There was enough meat on the whale to feed everyone for many weeks.

And so, the people became lazy. The giant continued to chop their wood and stoke their fires. If the meat ran low, then he would go out hunting once again.

"It is good you came," the people said. "What would we do without you?"

Maushop became frustrated. He could see that he was doing everything for them.

One day, he decided it was time to leave. Before he did, he taught the people the skills they would need to become better builders and hunters.

"Why do we need these skills?" they asked. "You are much stronger and wiser than us."

"Because I am leaving," he said sadly. "And you must now fend for yourselves."

He climbed the nearest mountain and took the largest rocks from its summit. Then he hurled these into the sea. They made a pathway of stepping stones. The giant waved goodbye, then—with mighty strides—he leapt from stone to stone and headed out to sea.

The Wampanoag tribe never saw him again. At that moment, they realized they had taken the giant for granted. From that day on, the people worked harder to be self-sufficient.

107

Responding to a Text

What three things do the Wampanoag tribe ask Maushop to help them with?

1. ....

2. ....

3. ....

What do you think Maushop is thinking when the people keep asking him to do things? Color in the thought bubble you agree with.

1. I'm hungry and want something to eat.

2. It's not fair that I am doing everything.

3. I am mighty and strong.

What does the word **flimsy** mean in the sentence below?

He saw that they were living in flimsy tepees that gave little protection from the cold and the wild beasts.

....

....

You could use a dictionary or thesaurus to help you.

Note for parent: Ask your child if they know of any other stories that feature giants. How do those giants compare with the character of Maushop?

Maushop uses his tremendous strength many times in the story. Describe one time he uses his strength to help others.

....

....

....

Circle the words that best describe how Maushop might be feeling at the end of the story.

delighted	sad	shy
frightened	frustrated	nervous

What lesson did the giant want to teach the Wampanoag tribe?

....

After the giant left, the Wampanoag tribe worked harder to be self-sufficient. Circle the best definition of **self-sufficient.**

1. to build and repair things

2. to look after yourself without needing help

3. to travel on your own

4. to have too much of something

Icarus and Daedalus

A Greek Myth

A long time ago, there lived an amazing inventor. His name was Daedalus. There wasn't a problem he couldn't solve. King Minos, who ruled the island of Crete, asked Daedalus to design him a prison for a fearsome creature known as the Minotaur. Daedalus agreed to the challenge and devised a complex maze of winding corridors. He called it the labyrinth—and if anyone entered, they would never be able to find their way out again.

Only Daedalus and his son, Icarus, knew the secret of the labyrinth. King Minos didn't want them to tell anyone, so he made them prisoners on the island. Daedalus tried to think of a way of escaping. He told Icarus to collect as many feathers as he could. Then he made two pairs of wings by sticking the feathers to a frame using wax.

"Now we can escape," said Daedalus. "But remember, do not fly too close to the sun!"

They went to the rooftop of their prison and waited for the strong winds to rush down from the mountains. Then they flapped their wings and took off into the sky!

They soared across the sparkling ocean. Icarus had never seen anything so beautiful. He flew higher and higher, excited by his sudden freedom. But he flew so high that the sun melted the wax on his wings. Icarus fell from the sky and plunged into the sea. He was never seen again.

Note for parent: You may wish to read about the myth of "Theseus and the Minotaur" to find out more about the characters and locations mentioned in this story.

Number these statements in the order that they happen in the story.

☐ Daedalus makes two pairs of wings.

☐ King Minos asks Daedalus to create a maze.

☐ Icarus is warned not to fly too close to the sun.

☐ Daedalus and Icarus become prisoners.

☐ Icarus collects feathers for his father.

☐ Daedalus and Icarus use their wings to escape the island of Crete.

☐ Icarus falls from the sky and plunges into the sea.

☐ Daedalus designs a complex maze. He calls it the labyrinth.

☐ The sun melts the wax on Icarus's wings.

Icarus
(ik-uh-rus)

Deadalus
(deh-duh-lus)

Minotaur
(min-o-tar)

labyrinth
(lab-er-rinth)

The Baobab Tree

An African Folktale

The god Thora had a wonderful garden. At the center of this garden was a talking tree—the baobab tree. Thora hoped that the tree would sing his praises every day—thanking him for the beautiful sunshine that warmed its leaves and the soothing rain that quenched its thirst. But the tree was grumpy and all it did was moan!

"Why am I not taller than the acacia tree?" the baobab grumbled.

"To be tall is not everything," replied Thora. "Be grateful for your arching branches."

The tree still wasn't happy.

"Why am I not as beautiful as the butterfly tree?" the baobab whined.

"To be beautiful is not everything," replied Thora. "Be grateful for your hardy bark."

The tree continued to moan.

"Why do I not have fruit like the marula tree?" the baobab groaned.

Thora was getting tired of all the complaining, so he gifted the baobab tree with fruit—juicy and nutritious. But the tree still wasn't happy.

"Why am I not as colorful as the red blossom?" the baobab griped.

Thora shook his fists in rage. He regretted ever making a talking tree! So, he picked up the tree and threw it out of his heavenly garden. The tree flew through the air and landed down on earth—head first! It was stuck in the ground with its roots in the air. And that is the way it has grown ever since.

Note for parent: This African folktale is one of many that seeks to explain the strange appearance of the baobab tree, which looks like its roots are growing in the air!

Read the sentences below. Write whether each is true or false.

The baobab tree was grateful and happy.   ....

Thora wanted the tree to praise to him.   ....

The baobab wanted fruit like the acacia tree.   ....

The butterfly tree is very beautiful.   ....

Thora regretted making a talking tree.   ....

The baobab tree landed upside down.   ....

The baobab tree can talk—but it isn't very good with words. Help the tree by finding these words in the story and explaining their meaning.

arching   ....

hardy   ....

nutritious ....

The Fox and the Stork

An Aesop's Fable

Sneaky Fox wanted to play a trick on Stork.

"Please, come over for dinner," Fox sneered.

"Oh, that's very nice of you," said Stork. "How lovely!"

Fox knew that Stork's favorite food was fish soup, so he spent all day fishing by the river and caught lots of delicious fish.

Once it got to dinnertime, Stork could smell the delicious soup wafting out of Fox's home. She couldn't wait to try it!

But Stork was in for a surprise. The sly fox had served up the soup in shallow dishes. He knew that Stork would not be able to get a drop of soup because of her very long beak. But the cunning fox lapped up all of his soup.

"How yummy!" he said. "What a shame you can't have any!"

The stork did not like Fox's mean trick. She went home hungry and sad. All night long, she thought about how she might teach him a lesson. The next morning, Stork invited Fox over for dinner.

The fox arrived and was very hungry.

"I have rabbit stew for you," said the stork.

Fox licked his lips. Rabbit stew was his favorite. However, Stork served the stew in tall jars. The stork could easily get to the food with her long beak, but the fox couldn't reach it with his short snout. Fox got very frustrated.

"This really isn't fair!" he growled.

And the Stork replied:

....

....

Note for parent: Encourage your child to think about the moral (or lesson) of the story Z—and what Stork might have said to Fox to explain this lesson.

1. Find and copy adjectives from the text which describe the fox. Can you think of any other words that would describe him?

....

....

2. What adjectives would you use to describe the stork?

....

....

3. Why did the stork feel sad?

....

....

4. Why did the fox feel angry?

....

....

Ideas for Your Own Story Writing

Sometimes a story idea might just pop into our head. But other times we might have to seek out a good idea. For example, we can:

I think the moon is made of cheese!

listen to others

read a news report

NEWS FLASH

Dog rescues hiker

I love funny stories!

read a book to inspire you

Write a story idea for these characters.

I'm always late. I wish I had more time!

I'm a terrible dragon. I've lost my fiery breath!

....

....

....

....

....

....

....

....

Note for parent: Encourage your child to keep an ideas notepad so that they can write down any interesting story ideas they discover.

Planning a Story

Before you write a story, it is a good idea to plan ahead.
Every good story has a number of important pieces.
As we fit them together, our story starts to take shape!

This is how we might
plan the story of
Little Red Riding Hood.

Main character	Setting	Goal	Problem	Ending
Little Red Riding Hood	the woods	take a picnic to Grandma	the Big Bad Wolf	Red Riding Hood outsmarts the Big Bad Wolf!

Do you have an idea for a story?
Plan it out using the jigsaw pieces.

Main character	Setting	Goal	Problem	Ending

Note for parent: Look together at some familiar fairy tales. Identify the different elements (characters, setting, goals, problem, ending/conclusion).

117

Describing Characters

Characters are the people, animals, or creatures that appear in a story. When we describe a character, we want to tell our reader something about them.

Read these character descriptions.

Mary Meek didn't have any friends, and she liked it that way. The other girls in class were always doing things she didn't enjoy, like talking about clothes or hanging out at the mall. Mary liked to read. She always had her nose in a book. The stories helped her to forget she was in a wheelchair. When she was reading, she could imagine she was somewhere else—solving a mystery or saving the day.

Greta Gump loved to remind people that she was the best—the best at getting into trouble. Every breaktime she would be bullying her next victim. She never smiled or laughed. Her freckled face would always be crunched up like a grumpy old man's. Everyone was afraid of her—even Charlie Clout, who said he once arm-wrestled a bear. If you saw Greta coming, then it was better to hide.

1. Which character do you think could be the hero in a story? Explain why.

....

....

....

2. Which character do you think could be the villain in a story? Explain why.

....

....

....

3. Which character is more likely to be:

boastful ....

imaginative ....

shy ....

angry ....

Note for parent: Ask your child to describe some storybook characters that they are familiar with. Explore what makes those characters memorable and interesting.

Creating a Character

Describe a character you would like to write about in a story. They could be a person, an animal, a robot, an alien—whatever you want to imagine!

Character's name:

....

Age: ....

Where do they live?

....

....

What do they like to do?

....

What are they afraid of?

....

Who is their best friend?

....

What do they want more than anything else?

....

Note for parent: Explore different ways of making a character unique—such as an unusual name, an aspect of their appearance, a favorite saying, and so on.

119

Settings

A setting is where the action of a story takes place. The setting for this story is a forest.

The bat led them deeper into the forest, flying with ease between the bent, twisted tree trunks. Zack and Zoe struggled to keep up, having a hard time avoiding the many spidery roots and slippery puddles of mud. Soon the ground began to drop steeply. The air became thick and damp. The surrounding trees were covered in slimy moss and dangling cobwebs.

Find and circle the adjectives in the story above.
A good description can help us to picture the scene. Draw what you think the forest would look like.

Write down some more adjectives to describe the forest you have drawn.

....

....

Note for parent: When writing a description of a place, encourage your child to imagine it through their senses and then use adjectives to describe it.

Story Openings

A good story opening should grab our attention. Circle the opening lines that you think are the most exciting.

Melanie was washing the dishes.

I looked up and there was a dinosaur!

A loud bang woke Sam from his slumber.

The old lady was waving at me.

We can also use the start of our story to explain our character's goal. What story goals do you think these characters might have?

I want to win the tournament.

Note for parent: Look together at the opening lines of favorite books. Consider how they grab and hold the reader's attention, and introduce the main character.

121

Conflict and Danger

A story would be very boring if there wasn't a problem or obstacle for a hero to overcome. Describe how these heroes might beat these challenges.

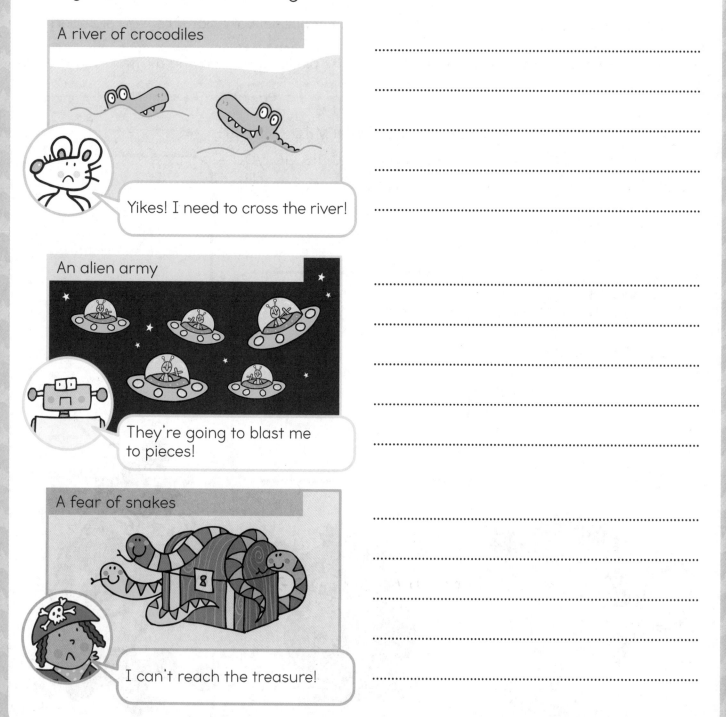

A river of crocodiles

Yikes! I need to cross the river!

An alien army

They're going to blast me to pieces!

A fear of snakes

I can't reach the treasure!

Note for parent: Choose a character, such as a knight or a pirate, then encourage your child to imagine different story obstacles that character might face.

Story Endings

Read the story.

There once lived a king who was very rich. Even though he had rooms full of gold and jewels, he still wanted more. One day, while travelling around his kingdom, he met an old beggar. Reluctantly, the king gave the beggar a gold coin. The beggar was so grateful that he offered the king a single wish. The king thought the old beggar was joking, but he decided to play along.

"Okay, I want everything I touch to turn into gold!" Sure enough, the wish came true. When the king returned home, he touched his front door and it turned to gold. And so did the staircase in his hall, the table in his dining room, the seat in his throne room...everything became gold! But there was a problem. When the king picked up his food, it turned to gold. When he hugged his son, the boy turned to gold.

"What have I done?" gasped the king. "This is not a blessing. It is a curse!"

Now choose a story ending. Will it be:
A **surprise** ending—something unexpected happens!
A **happy** ending—everything ends well for the main character.
A **lesson** ending—the character learns something.

Write an ending for the story above.

The King touched Him self then the turn in to gold

Note for parent: A good story ending shows how a main character has changed over the course of the story in order to overcome problems.

123

Which Tense?

When writing a story, we can choose to write in the present tense or the past tense.

Present tense—the action is happening now.
   I can't find my shoes. I'll be late for school.

Past tense—the action has already happened.
   I couldn't find my shoes. I was late for school.

Chris needs help with his story. He wants his story to be in the past tense. Underline any sentences he will need to change.

Frog was sitting on his favorite lily pad. He is catching flies with his long sticky tongue. Yum, yum! He is feeling happy.

Suddenly, he heard a loud splash behind him. He turned to see an enormous crocodile. It was headed straight toward him.

Frog quickly hops from lily pad to lily pad. He didn't want to get eaten by the crocodile.

Then there was an even bigger splash. Frog sees an elephant wading into the water. The elephant was bigger than the crocodile. He lifts up his trunk and trumpets loudly. The sound scared the crocodile who swam away.

Frog was happy that he was safe. "Thank you, Mr. Elephant!"

Note for parent: Remind your child of common past tense suffixes, and how you could correct this story so that it reads in the past tense.

A Counting Rhyme

Add your own words to complete this counting rhyme for a younger member of your family, or a friend. Practice reading your poem out loud and perform it for them.

Over in the meadow in a new little hive

Lived an old mother queen bee and her honeybees five.

"Hum," said the mother.

"We hum," said the five.

So they hummed and were glad in their new little hive.

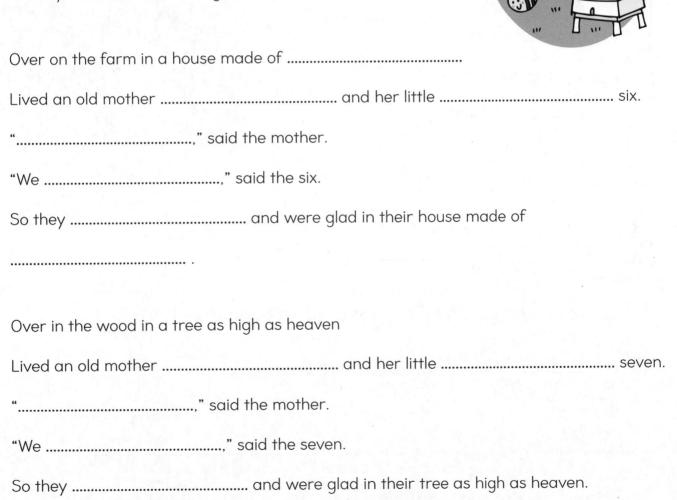

Over on the farm in a house made of ....

Lived an old mother .... and her little .... six.

".............................," said the mother.

"We ....," said the six.

So they .... and were glad in their house made of

....

Over in the wood in a tree as high as heaven

Lived an old mother .... and her little .... seven.

".............................," said the mother.

"We ....," said the seven.

So they .... and were glad in their tree as high as heaven.

Note for parent: This poem is based on the counting rhyme, "Over in the Meadow." Help your child to choose suitable words that will follow the framework shown in the first stanza.

125

The Owl and the Pussy Cat

Read these stanzas taken from the famous poem, then answer the questions.

Pussy said to the Owl, "You elegant fowl!

How charmingly sweet you sing!

O let us be married! Too long we have tarried:

But what shall we do for a ring?"

They sailed away, for a year and a day,

To the land where the Bong-tree grows

And there in a wood a Piggy-wig stood

With a ring at the end of his nose,

His nose,

His nose,

With a ring at the end of his nose.

1. Circle all the pairs of rhyming words you can find.

2. What does Pussy like about the Owl?

    He sings   He sings good

3. Underline the words that mean "We have waited too long."

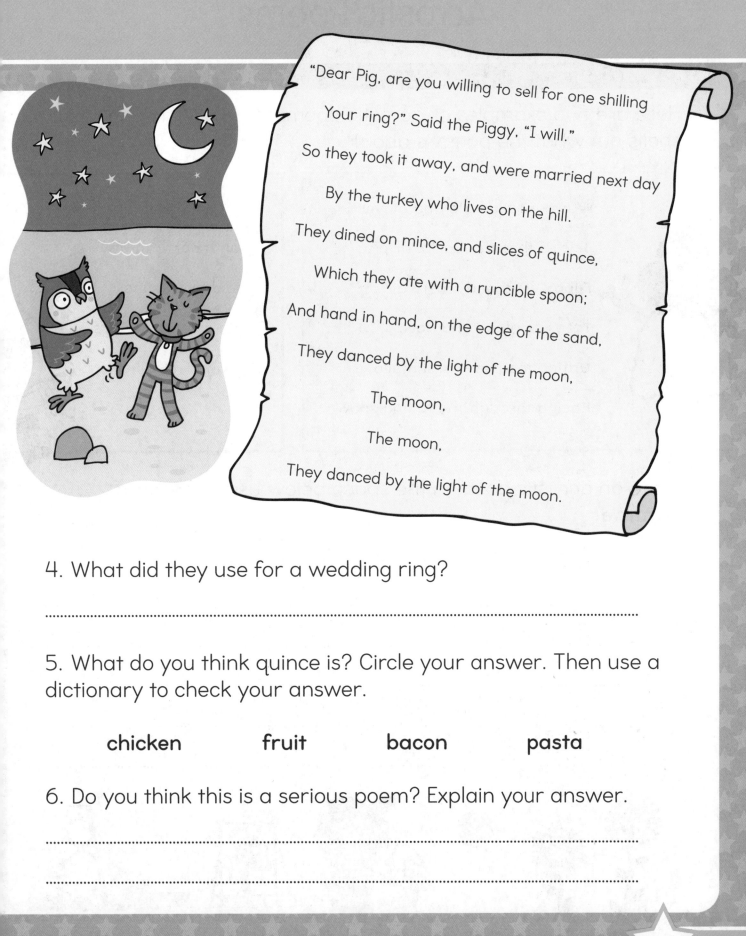

"Dear Pig, are you willing to sell for one shilling

Your ring?" Said the Piggy, "I will."

So they took it away, and were married next day

By the turkey who lives on the hill.

They dined on mince, and slices of quince,

Which they ate with a runcible spoon;

And hand in hand, on the edge of the sand,

They danced by the light of the moon,

The moon,

The moon,

They danced by the light of the moon.

4. What did they use for a wedding ring?

....

5. What do you think quince is? Circle your answer. Then use a dictionary to check your answer.

      chicken   **fruit**   **bacon**   **pasta**

6. Do you think this is a serious poem? Explain your answer.

....

....

Acrostic Poems

Here are two examples of acrostic poems. A letter on each line spells out what the poem is about.

Warm woolly hats and gloves

icicles that drip, drip, drip

nippy wind and frosty air

trees so black and bare

eating toasted marshmallows

racing through the falling snow

kites in the sky

on a spr**i**ng day

held by s**t**ring

on color**e**d wings

don't **s**ail away

Write an acrostic poem in the space below using the word **summer**.

Sun shining

ur ~~eating~~ Playing

makeny friens

mam is baking

eating ~~out~~ cooking

re blooming flowers

Note for parent: In an acrostic poem, some of the letters on each line spell out a word when you read downward. The word is usually the subject of the poem.

Rhyme and Rhythm

When writing poetry, we can match the number of beats (or syllables) in each line. This nonsense poem has six beats on each line. Clap along as you read it out loud.

There once was a big fish

Sitting on a blue dish.

He looked me in the eye

And said, "I'm rather shy.

If you would hear my plea,

Put me back in the sea!"

The words at the end of each pair of sentences rhyme together.

Add rhyming sentences to this poem. Don't worry if the sentences don't make sense—it can be a nonsense poem!

There once was a white cat

....

On his back was a flea

....

He scratched all day and night

....

And howled and made a din

....

Note for parent: Use a rhyming dictionary to find words that rhyme with cat, flea, night, and din. For added challenge, try to create sentences with six beats.

129

Fiction and Nonfiction

Fiction books contain made-up stories with characters and dialogue. Nonfiction books contain information and facts.

Decide if these books are fiction (made up) or nonfiction (fact).

1. **ALL ABOUT SPACE** → .... nonfiction ....

2. **SUPER KID TO THE RESCUE** → ....

3. **SAFE CYCLING** → ....

4. **THE MAGIC CARPET** → ....

5. **MAPS OF THE WORLD** → ....

6. **SCIENCE PROBLEMS** → ....

Which book do you think these extracts are taken from?

1. Aladdin saw that the cave was filled with treasure. Quickly, he stuffed his pockets with gold and jewels. Then he caught sight of a shiny lamp and an old, tattered carpet.

....

2. Many planets have moons. Some have more than one. Jupiter, the largest planet in our solar system, has sixty-three! Earth only has one moon.

....

3. Braking is an important skill to master. Make sure that you apply pressure evenly to both brakes. You can practice this by walking next to your bike and pulling on the brakes to make it stop.

....

Finding Information

Read this extract from a book about space. Then answer the questions.

THE PLANETS

At the present time, scientists know of eight planets in our solar system. Like Earth, they travel around the Sun. The inner planets (those nearest the Sun) are: Mercury, Venus, Earth, and Mars. The outer planets (those farther away from the Sun) are: Jupiter, Saturn, Uranus, and Neptune. The biggest planet in our solar system is the gas giant, Jupiter. It is approximately eleven times the size of Earth! Pluto was once considered the ninth planet in the solar system. However, it is now considered a "dwarf planet."

1. Why do you think the author has used the phrase "At the present time...?"

....

2. How many planets are there in our solar system?

....

3. Name the outer planets.

....

4. Which planet is fourth from the sun?

....

5. What is the name of the biggest planet in our solar system?

....

Note for parent: This activity will give your child practice in using a text to find facts and details to answer questions.

131

A Biography

Read the biography, then answer the questions.

I Sell the Shadow to Support the Substance.

SOJOURNER TRUTH.

Sojourner Truth (1797–1883)

Early Years

Sojourner Truth was born in 1797 on a farm in the state of New York. Her birth name was Isabella Baumfree. Because both of her parents were slaves, Sojourner was born a slave. At the age of nine, she was sold to a new owner for $100.

Around the age of 18, Sojourner fell in love with a slave named Robert. Sadly, the couple were not allowed to marry because they had different owners. Instead, Isabella was forced to marry another slave named Thomas. They had a son and two daughters.

After many years of harsh slavery, Sojourner was finally promised her freedom. However, her cruel owner later changed his mind. Sojourner was very upset so she ran away with her youngest daughter, Sophia.

Saving Her Son

Sojourner found refuge with the Van Wagenen family in New Paltz, New York. They were kind to her and looked after her. Not long after, many slaves started to gain their freedom, including Sojourner and her daughters. However, Sojourner's son had not been so lucky. He was still a slave and had been sold to a new owner.

Sojourner decided to go to court to get her son back. This took a lot of courage, but she won her case. She was the first African-American woman to ever take a white man to court and win. Sojourner and her son were reunited at last!

Note for parent: Sojourner Truth was an American abolitionist. She changed her name to Sojourner Truth because a sojourner is someone who travels from place to place.

A National Hero

Sojourner could not read or write, but she was an excellent speaker. She began traveling around the country, telling people what it was like to be a slave. It was around this time that she decided to change her name to Sojourner Truth. In 1851 she gave a famous speech called "Ain't I a Woman?". She became so famous she even got to meet President Abraham Lincoln at the White House!

Sojourner Truth dedicated her life to ending slavery. Her stories and speeches helped many people understand how cruel slavery was. She died on November 26, 1883 at the age of 86.

1. When and where was Sojourner Truth born?

....

2. Why was Sojourner Truth born a slave?

....

3. In the second section, what do you think the word "refuge" means?

....

4. Why did Sojourner go to court?

....

5. What useful skill did Sojourner Truth use?

....

6. Why do you think Sojourner Truth is important?

....

....

....

Text and Illustration

Title ....

The cheetah is the fastest land animal. It can reach astonishing speeds of up to

74 mph. Its nearest rival is the springbok, a type of antelope that lives in southern

Africa. It can reach speeds of 55 mph. Close behind is the lion, which is the second

fastest wild cat. But, unlike the cheetah, a lion can only run for very short distances

before tiring out. Next is the jackrabbit, that leaps and zigzags quickly to confuse

predators. At 44 mph, the jackrabbit just beats the kangaroo—but the kangaroo

is close behind, and what it lacks in speed, it makes up for with its huge jumps.

A kangaroo can jump 25 feet in a single bound!

a. ....

b. ....

c. ....

d. ....

e. ....

1. Give the text on the opposite page an interesting title.

2. Label the illustrations using the text to help you.

3. Use the text and the illustrations to answer the following questions:

a. What does "mph" mean?

....

b. Which land animal runs the fastest?

....

c. Which animal can reach a speed of 55 mph per hour?

....

d. How does the jackrabbit escape predators?

....

e. Which animals are slower runners than the lion?

....

f. How are the illustrations useful in explaining the text?

....

....

Labeling a Map

Use the text to help you label the theme park map.

OUR TRIP TO ADVENTURE LAND!

We went through the front entrance and headed left to Splash Canyon. We got very wet on the log flume. Then we followed the path into the Spooky Forest. Mom was too scared to come on the ghost train with us! It was lunchtime, so we went to the Planet X restaurant for space burgers, then we rode the rocket rollercoaster in Future Zone. We ended the day by watching a magic show in the Enchanted Valley. We didn't have time to go to the Pirate Cove, but we will next time!

1. ....

2. ....

3. ....

4. ....

5. ....

6. ....

Note for parent: Encourage your child to look for clues in the text to help them correctly label the locations on the map.

Big Ideas

The human body is an amazing machine. Let's start with the skeleton. Did you know that your skeleton has over 200 bones? They are what keep your body's shape, let you move around, and also protect all your vital organs. Every organ in the body has a special job to do. Imagine what it would be like if we had no lungs to allow us to breathe, or no brain to help us to think! And let's not forget our muscles, that allow us to walk, run, jump, and more— and our skin, which wraps us all up to keep everything safe inside!

1. The main idea is what the author most wants us to know about a topic. Circle the main idea of the text.

2. Supporting details tell us more about the main idea. Circle two supporting details from the box below that match with the text.

Every organ has a special job to do.   We can stick out our tongue.

Calcium is good for our bones.   Your skeleton protects your vital organs.

3. This text is missing a title. What title would you give it?

....

Note for parent: This activity will give your child practice in identifying the main idea of a text and its supporting details.

137

Using a Table of Contents

We can quickly find the information we need by looking at the contents page of a book. This is the table of contents from a book called "My First Aquarium."

Where would you look to find out...

1. Where to set up your fish tank.

2. What to do if a fish gets a disease.

3. What type of fish food is best?

4. How to decorate your tank.

Note for parent: This activity gives your child practice in using text features to locate relevant information efficiently.

Using Clues to Find Meaning

Read the text carefully, then write what you think the highlighted words mean. You can use a dictionary to check your answers.

There are around 300 **species** of octopus. They are well-known for having eight **tentacles**. Each tentacle has two rows of suckers, which are used to attach to **prey**.

Octopuses have three main **defense** tools. The first is ink. If threatened, an octopus can squirt a dark cloud of ink into the water. This can scare away **predators**.

Secondly, octopuses can regrow their limbs. If an octopus becomes trapped, it can tear off one or more tentacles to escape. The lost limbs will slowly regrow over time.

Finally, octopuses can **camouflage** themselves. They do this by changing the color of their skin.

camouflage
to hide something by matching its color or pattern to its surroundings
....

defense
....

tentacles
....

prey
....

predators
....

species
....

Busy Bees

Honeybees live in groups called colonies. Their home is called a hive, where all the bees work together as a team. Each bee has a special job to do.

Queen bee
The queen bee is the largest bee in the colony. She is the boss of the hive and the only bee that can lay eggs. A queen bee can lay up to 2,500 eggs a day! After a few days, the larvae hatch.

Drones
The drones are the only male bees in the colony. They never leave the hive and are responsible for mating with the queen bee so she can make more eggs.

Worker bees
The worker bees are female. They have lots of jobs to do. As well as building the hive and helping protect it from attackers, they also gather nectar and pollen from flowers.

Nectar is taken back to the hive where it is turned into honey. The bees store this honey in honeycombs. Pollen is also stored by the bees and is mixed with honey to produce "bee bread." This is a vital food for the bees and the growing larvae.

When worker bees are busy collecting, they also spread pollen from flower to flower. This pollen helps plants reproduce and is called "pollination." Because plants need bees, they try to attract them with their color and scent.

It is not just plants that need bees. Lots of fruit and vegetables come from plants that the bees pollinate. We also love to eat the honey the bees produce. So in many ways we need bees, too!

1. Read the facts below. Write whether each is true or false.

a. The queen bee and worker bees are female. ....

b. Drones are the largest bees in the colony. ....

c. Bees collect honey and pollen from flowers. ....

d. Plants use their colorful flowers and scent to attract bees. ....

2. What are some of the jobs that worker bees do?

....

....

3. Why are bees important to us?

....

....

4. Did you know honeybees are great dancers? Worker bees do a special dance, known as a "waggle dance." Use books and/or the Internet to find out more. Then write a paragraph to explain why this dance is important.

....

....

....

....

Butterfly Life Cycle

Complete the sentences using the words from the labels on the left. Then, number the sentences so they are in the correct order to describe the life cycle of a butterfly.

caterpillar

eggs

chrysalis

butterfly

☐ After about 5 days, an .... egg .... will hatch into a small ....

☐ The .... must eat a lot of leaves in order to grow.

[I] First, the female butterfly lays her .... eggs .... on a leaf.

☐ After a few weeks, the caterpillar surrounds its body with a hard shell called a ....

☐ When the .... is ready to emerge, the .... splits open.

☐ Finally, the .... must wait for its wings to dry out before it can fly away.

☐ Inside the chrysalis the .... slowly changes into a ....

Note for parent: This activity will give your child practice in making logical connections between sentences to form a sequence.

Proofreading

Tom has written a report about the Galapagos Islands, but he has made some mistakes in his writing. Can you proofread his report? Use the proofreading key below to mark the errors that need correcting.

PROOFREADING KEY

☰	capitalize	The galapagos islands are a national park. ☰ ☰
/	change to lower case	The green ~~S~~ea turtle is a common sight.
⊙	add a period	Many unique animal species live on the islands⊙
◯	correct spelling	Marine iguanas are (excelant) swimmers.
✗	take out a word	The islands lie along the ~~the~~ equator.

Here is Tom's report:

The Galapagos Islands are a group of 19 islands in the pacific Ocean. They lie off the west coast of South america. They were made from active volcanoes and the the largest is called Sierra Negra on the island of Isabela The islands are Famous for there many native animals, such as marine iguanas, penguins, sea lions, and Giant Tortoises.

Note for parent: Encourage your child to regularly check their own work and mark up any mistakes using the appropriate proofreading marks.

143

Information Writing

Here is an informational text about chocolate. Read and number the paragraphs in the correct order to make sense to the reader.

The opening sentence introduces the topic.

1	Chocolate is one of the world's best-loved foods—and it all comes from a tiny bean!

Organize facts into paragraphs.

	In 1847, Francis Fry decided to make solid chocolate. He mixed cocoa powder with butter and sugar. When the mixture cooled, it hardened into chocolate bars. Chocolate makers have been experimenting ever since. In 1900, the first Hershey Milk Chocolate Bar was sold!

Facts give further information.

	Chocolate comes from the cacao tree, which grows in tropical areas. The tree produces pods that are full of hard and bitter-tasting beans. Over 2,000 years ago, the Aztec people used these beans to make a drink.

This is a linking phrase.

	Hundreds of years later, in the 1500s, the Spanish discovered the Aztecs' chocolate drink. But the drink was too bitter for their taste so they added sugar and heated it up. The Spanish had just invented hot chocolate!

This is a linking word.

The concluding sentence refers back to the topic.

5	New chocolate bars are still being invented today—who knows what flavors we will be trying out in the future!

Note for parent: Help your child to identify the correct order of the paragraphs, using details from the text, and finding the linking words and phrases.

Writing an Informational Text

Choose a topic to research and write about. You can use the writing frame below to help organize your writing.

Use linking words and phrases to connect your sentences and paragraphs together.

 Pandas

 The North Pole

 Teeth

Here are some useful words and phrases that you can use:

and   more   but   also   after   then   next   because   when

Introductory sentence

....

Paragraph I

....

....

....

Paragraph 2

....

....

....

Concluding sentence

....

Note for parent: Encourage your child to look back at the example on the opposite page to help organize their own informational text.

145

Frozen Banana Lollipops

Oh dear, Molly's favorite recipe is smudged. Help her to fill in the missing details.

Equipment

knife

cutting board

4 lollipop sticks

baking paper

_____ tray

jug

Ingredients
(serves 4)

2 bananas

half cup of plain yogurt

bar of _____

caramel sauce or

raspberry sauce

chocolate chips

candy sprinkles

Instructions

1. Peel the _____.

2. Cut each banana in half.

3. Push each piece of banana onto a lollipop stick.

4. Pour the plain _____ into a jug.

5. Dip each banana lolly into the yogurt to cover it.

6. Line a baking tray with baking paper.

7. Lay the banana lollipops on the _____ paper.

8. Put the _____ in the freezer for an hour.

9. Melt the chocolate bar. (Ask an adult to do this for you!)

10. Dip the end of each banana lollipop in the _____.

11. Sprinkle over your choice of toppings and sauce.

12. Place back in the freezer until the chocolate has set.

Note for parent: With your help and supervision, encourage your child to try out the recipe by following each of the steps to make their own lollipops!

Writing a Recipe

Write a recipe for your own favorite snack—it could be a sandwich, a milkshake, a cake—whatever tasty food you want to teach someone else how to make!

Equipment

....

....

....

....

....

Number the instructions.

Write in the present tense.

Instructions

....

....

....

....

....

....

....

....

....

....

Use short sentences.

Ingredients

....

....

....

....

....

....

Start each sentence with a verb.

Note for parent: Remind your child to give clear step-by-step instructions for someone else to follow. Use the example on the opposite page for reference.

147

Reading an Opinion Piece

Charlie has written an opinion piece about how much he loves cats.

Cats Are the Best!

In my opinion, cats make better pets than dogs.

Firstly, cats don't need to be taken for walks. My best friend, Carl, walks his dog every day, even when the weather is bad. But a cat only goes outside when it wants to. My cat loves playing in the yard when it is a nice day. Sometimes, she likes to sit on the roof of the shed and watch the birds. When it rains, she stays inside and sleeps in her basket.

Secondly, because a cat can clean itself, you don't have to wash a cat and it never smells. Carl's dog loves to roll around in the mud. He likes getting dirty and smelly! Cats prefer to stay nice and clean.

Finally, cats don't make a lot of noise. My cat likes to purr softly when I tickle her tummy or stroke her back. Dogs can bark a lot when they get excited. I know Carl is always apologizing to his neighbor, Miss Hall. She doesn't like noise when she is doing her yoga in the back yard!

In conclusion, I think if you want a good pet, then you should definitely choose a cat!

Note for parent: An effective opinion piece states the opinion clearly in the opening sentence, then sets out reasons to support that opinion, backed up by examples.

Responding to an Opinion Piece

Charlie states his opinion clearly in his opening sentence. What is his opinion?

....

What three reasons does Charlie give to support his opinion?

1. ....

....

2. ....

....

3. ....

....

Charlie gives some examples to support his reasons.
Circle the reasons below that match with the text.

a. Dogs can get dirty and smelly.

b. Cats help to keep mice away.

c. Cats like to purr softly.

d. Dogs need to be walked, even in bad weather.

Do you agree or disagree with Charlie? Give one reason to support your opinion.

....

....

Note for parent: This activity encourages your child to carefully study a text in order to answer questions. They are also asked to give their own point of view.

149

Different Points of View

A water park is going to be built in the popular seaside town of Sand Beach. There will be lots of different slides and rides! But most of the local woodland will need to be chopped down to make room for the water park.

Alyce and Paul have different opinions about the water park.

I say no to the water park!

I don't think they should chop down our woodland. Many people like to walk in the woods. I take my dog there. There are lots of animals that live in the woods, too. They won't be happy to lose their home!

I say yes to the water park!

I can't wait for a water park. It will be so much fun to be able to go there at weekends. I hear there are going to be some awesome slides. The beach can get really crowded and not everyone likes swimming in the ocean.

If you lived in Sand Beach, what would your opinion be?

I think ....

....

because ....

....

....

Note for parent: This activity encourages your child to imagine a scenario and then distinguish their own point of view from that of others.

Writing an Opinion Piece

Choose one of these topics to write an opinion piece.

Summer is better than winter

All kids should have a cell phone

Use linking words and phrases to connect your sentences and paragraphs together.

Here are some useful words and phrases that you can use:

| first | and | but | also | because | secondly | when | finally | since | therefore |

In my opinion ....

....

(Reason 1) ....

....

(Reason 2) ....

....

(Reason 3) ....

....

In conclusion ....

....

....

Note for parent: The writing frame will help your child to structure their opinion piece with an opening sentence, three reasons to support their opinion, then a concluding statement.

151

Catchphrases

Every good ad has a catchphrase. When we remember and hear a catchphrase, we immediately think of the product.

Which products are these catchphrases describing? Match the catchphrases to these products.

1. **STEP OUT IN STYLE!**

2. 8 out of 10 dogs love them.

3. CRUNCHY TASTY GOODNESS!

4. *Scent of a Superstar*

5. Are you ready to **SPARKLE?**

6. **THE FASTEST TOY ON EARTH!**

Note for parent: Listen and look for examples of persuasive phrases in ads on TV and product packaging.

Writing an Ad

Donut Dreams have asked you to help them plan out an ad. The aim is to make people want to visit their store and try out their new flavor.

Start by writing a snappy title to grab the attention!

What makes Donut Dreams the best? Think of three reasons.

Try our new flavor...

What special offer can we make?

Now, let's think of a great catchphrase that people will remember!

Note for parent: Encourage your child to think about how they can use superlative language in their ad, for example, the greatest, biggest, tastiest, coolest, etc.

153

Number Skills

Helping Your Child

- The activities in this section will help your child to learn how to add and subtract numbers within 1,000, understand place value, and solve word problems.

- Your child will learn how to multiply and divide numbers within 100, recognize patterns in numbers, and solve equations involving an unknown number.

- Children will learn how to use a number line and practice strategies for calculations involving larger numbers.

- Set aside time to do the activities together. Do a little at a time, so that your child enjoys learning.

- The answers begin on page 313.

Contents

Number Values

Numbers are made up of digits. Each digit has a value.

153 → one hundred
153 → five tens
153 → three ones

We can write it this way:

153 = 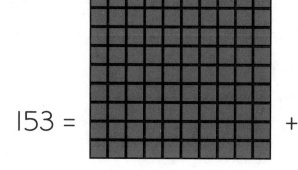 + 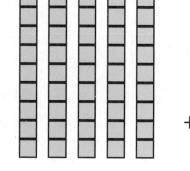 +

Write the number values in the boxes.

264 = 200 + 60 + 4   382 = ☐ + ☐ + ☐

401 = ☐ + ☐ + ☐   890 = ☐ + ☐ + ☐

637 = ☐ + ☐ + ☐   762 = ☐ + ☐ + ☐

Note for parent: This activity will help your child to recognize how the position of a digit determines its value.

Ordering Numbers

Write these numbers on the green ladder in descending order from the largest to the smallest.

80 22 90 73
10 64 56 38

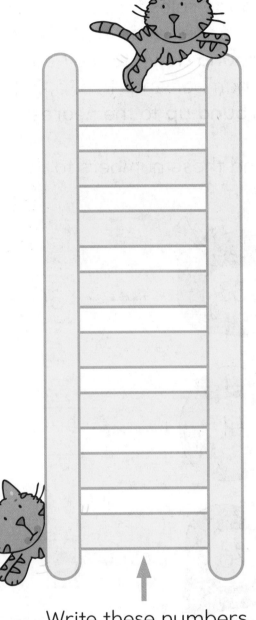

Write these numbers on the yellow ladder in ascending order from the smallest to the largest.

36 98 55 5
40 82 74 29

Note for parent: This activity will help your child to practice strategies for sorting and ordering numbers.

157

Rounding Numbers to the Nearest 10

Read the rules for rounding:
If a number ends in 1, 2, 3, or 4
we **round down** to the nearest ten.
If a number ends in 5, 6, 7, 8, or 9
we **round up** to the nearest ten.

Round these numbers to the nearest ten.

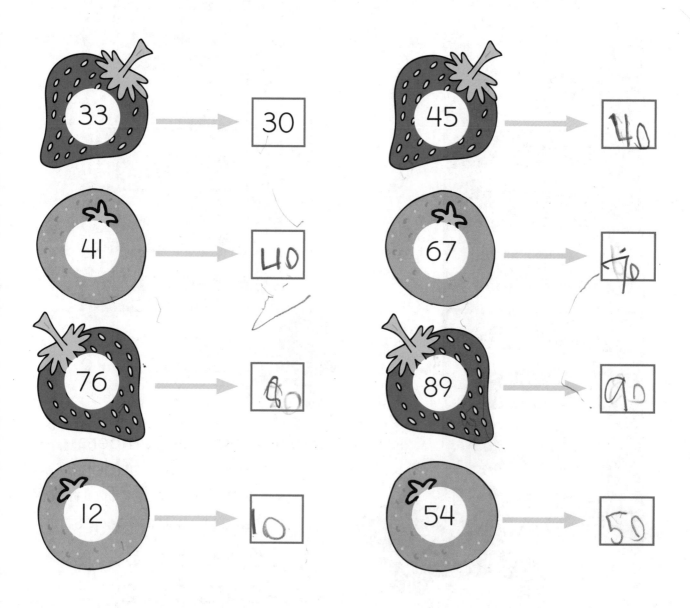

Note for parent: In the example above, you can explain that 33 is nearer to 30 than it is to 40.

Rounding Numbers to the Nearest 100

436 is closer to 400 than to 500.
436 is 400 rounded to the nearest hundred.

Use the number lines to round these numbers
to the nearest hundred.

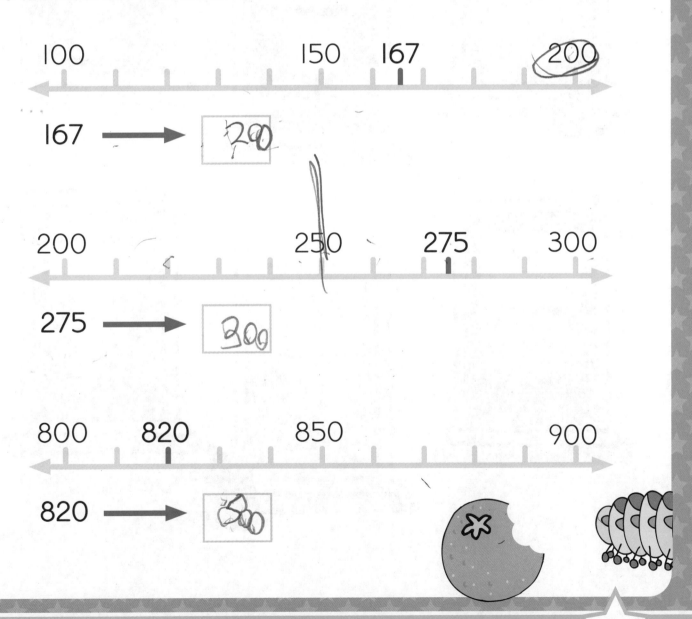

167 ⟶ 200

275 ⟶ 300

820 ⟶ 800

Note for parent: Rounding Numbers is a useful skill to use when checking or estimating answers. More on this later in the book.

Number Words

Write these words as numbers.

twelve
12

twenty
20

thirty-six
36

sixty-four
64

eighty-six
86

ninety-five
95

Note for parent: This activity helps children to recognize that numbers can also be written as words. For example, numbers are sometimes written as words in math problems.

Addition and Subtraction Patterns

If 3 + 6 = 9, then 30 + 60 = 90, and 300 + 600 = 900.

Fill in the missing numbers in the boxes.
Notice the pattern in the numbers.

2 + 7 = $\boxed{9}$ 5 + 4 = $\boxed{9}$

20 + 70 = $\boxed{90}$ $\boxed{}$

200 + 700 = $\boxed{900}$ $\boxed{500}$ + 400 = 900

Now try these subtractions. Fill in the missing numbers.

8 – 3 = $\boxed{5}$ 9 – 5 = $\boxed{4}$

80 – $\boxed{30}$ = 50 $\boxed{90}$ – 50 = 40

800 – 300 = $\boxed{500}$ 900 – $\boxed{500}$ = 400

1   2   3   4   5   6   7   8   9   10

10   30   50   70   90
  20   40   60   80   100

325 = 113

If you know that 5 + 4 = 9, then 9 – 4 = 5, and 9 – 5 = 4.

Try it out with these sums.

45 – 21

40 – 20 = 26

6 + 4 = 10   10 – 4 = $\boxed{6}$ 10 – 6 = $\boxed{4}$

8 + 7 = 15   15 – 7 = $\boxed{8}$ 15 – 8 = $\boxed{9}$

15 + 6 = 21   21 – 6 = $\boxed{15}$ 21 – 15 = $\boxed{6}$

22 + 7 = 29   29 – 7 = $\boxed{}$ 29 – 22 = $\boxed{7}$

38 + 2 = 40   40 – 2 = $\boxed{}$ 40 – 38 = $\boxed{2}$

51 + 8 = 59   59 – 8 = $\boxed{51}$ 59 – 51 = $\boxed{8}$

29 – 7
22

Word Problems

Solve these problems by adding or subtracting the numbers.

1. Jess scored 40 points in the first round. Ruby scored 25.

What was the difference in their scores?

.........15......... points difference

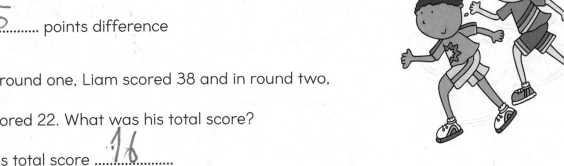

2. In round one, Liam scored 38 and in round two,

he scored 22. What was his total score?

Liam's total score ....16.......

3. Kelly's total score was 50 but she was later fined 25 points

for cheating in the first round! What was her final total?

Kelly's final total ....25.

4. Nizra scored 80 plus 10 plus 15. What was his total score?

Nizra's total .....115.......

5. Find the difference between Nizra's total and Kelly's.

........90........ points difference

Note for parent: Word problems such as these make math relevant in our lives.

163

Making 100

Draw circles around pairs of numbers that make 100 when added together.

$25 + 75$

$60 + 44$

$31 + 69$

$82 + 18$

$13 + 77$

$60 + 39$

$55 + 45$

$64 + 36$

100

$59 + 41$

$28 + 80$

Note for parent: Try this strategy—add the ones first. If they make ten, ask your child: do the tens, then add up to 90?

Doubles

What is 15 + 15?
To figure out what double 15 is ...

double 5   =   10
double 10 =   20
   total   =   30

Figure out these doubles.

double 6 = ~~42~~ ~~25~~ 12
double 20 = ~~22~~ 40
   total   = 52

double 7 = ~~40~~ 14
double 10 = ~~25~~ 20
   total   = 34

double 9 = 18
double 40 = 80
   total   = 89

double 5 = 10
double 30 = 60
   total   = 70

Note for parent: Discuss strategies, for example, 49 is one less than 50—so you could round up 49 to 50, double it, then subtract 2.

Pencil and Paper Addition

Sometimes with larger numbers, it is better to figure out sums using pencil and paper.

For example, if you want to add 65 and 27, you can write it like this:

$$65 + 27 = (60 + 20) + (5 + 7) = 80 + 12 = 92$$

Try these:

34 + 36 = 70

14 70

55 + 29 = 84

62 + 38 = 90

77 + 24 = 101

Pencil and Paper Subtraction

If you want to subtract 27 from 65, you can draw a number line and count up.

65 – 27

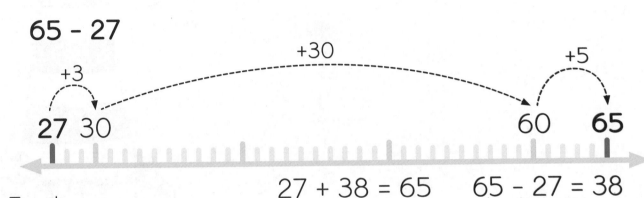

+3

+30

+5

27 30

60 **65**

27 + 38 = 65   65 – 27 = 38

Try these:

84 – 55 = ☐

2 ⓞ x

4 +

55   60

80   **84**

73 – 43 = 30

50

43   50

70

70 **73**

98 – 67 = ☐

67 70

90   **98**

Note for parent: This activity helps your child to see how addition and subtraction are related, and are reverse operations.

Addition with 100s, 10s, and Is

Find the sum of these numbers. Add the ones first, then the tens, then the hundreds.

Like this:

```
  156
+  42
-----
  198
```

Now try these:

```
  138        224          403
+  41       +  65        + 174
-----       -----        -----
                           577
```

```
  521        343          706
+ 262       + 344        + 242
-----       -----        -----
```

Note for parent: This activity shows your child an efficient method of addition.

Subtraction with Regrouping

Find the difference between these numbers.
Subtract the ones first, then the tens, then the
hundreds. Regroup if you need to.

Like this:

```
      2 16
   4 3 6
 - 2 1 7
 ─────────
   2 1 9
```

You can't take away 7 from 6, so you have to exchange
1 ten for 10 ones. This will give you 16 ones.
Now you can take 7 from 16.

Now try these:

```
    5 13
  5 6 3
 -2 1 5
 ──────
  3 4 8
```

```
    6 12
  8 7 2
 -2 3 8
 ──────
  6 3 4
```

```
   3 10 1
  4 1 5
 -2 9 5
 ──────
  1 2 0
```

```
    4 12
  5 2 9
 -2 8 5
 ──────
  2 4 4
```

```
    5 10
  9 6 0
 -2 1 5
 ──────
  7 4 5
```

```
    2 12
  9 3 6
 -2 1 8
 ──────
  7 2 4
```

Note for parent: If you can't subtract the bottom number from the top number, you have
to regroup by exchanging 1 ten for 10 ones and/or 1 hundred for 10 tens.

171

Repeated Addition

Sometimes we need to add together groups of objects.
For example:

5 + 5 + 5 =   3 groups of 5 =   3 x 5 =

The sign "x" means groups of, or multiplied by.

Try these repeated additions.
Write the missing numbers in the boxes.

2 + 2 + 2 + 2 = | 4 | groups of 2 | 4 | x 2 = | 8 |

3 + 3 + 3 + 3 = | | groups of 3 | | x 3 = | |

10 + 10 + 10 = | | groups of 10 | | x 10 = | |

5 + 5 + 5 + 5 + 5 = | | groups of 5 | | x 5 = | |

4 + 4 + 4 + 4 = | | groups of 4 | | x 4 = | |

6 + 6 + 6 = | | groups of 6 | | x 6 = | |

Note for parent: This activity will help your child to see multiplication as repeated addition.

Multiplying in Any Order

When we look at the circles below, we can see that:

   3 lots of 4 = 12 and 4 lots of 3 = 12

3 x 4 = 12   4 x 3 = 12

We can multiply the numbers in any order and the answers are the same!

Complete these multiplications.

4   x   5 = 20

5   x   4 = 20

3   x   7   = 21

7   x   3   = 21

2   x   10   = 20

10   x   2   = 20

Note for parent: From this activity, your child should begin to recognize that we can multiply the same numbers in any order and the answer will be the same.

Multiplying by 2

Count by twos. Color in the twos pattern in the number square.

1	2	3	4	5	6	7	8	9	10
11	12	13	14	15	16	17	18	19	20
21	22	23	24	25	26	27	28	29	30
31	32	33	34	35	36	37	38	39	40
41	42	43	44	45	46	47	48	49	50
51	52	53	54	55	56	57	58	59	60
61	62	63	64	65	66	67	68	69	70
71	72	73	74	75	76	77	78	79	80
81	82	83	84	85	86	87	88	89	90
91	92	93	94	95	96	97	98	99	100

Fill in the missing numbers in the twos pattern.

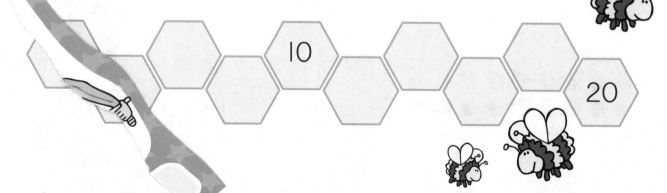

10

20

Multiplying by 3

Count by threes. Color in the threes pattern in the number square.

1	2	3	4	5	6	7	8	9	10
11	12	13	14	15	16	17	18	19	20
21	22	23	24	25	26	27	28	29	30
31	32	33	34	35	36	37	38	39	40
41	42	43	44	45	46	47	48	49	50
51	52	53	54	55	56	57	58	59	60
61	62	63	64	65	66	67	68	69	70
71	72	73	74	75	76	77	78	79	80
81	82	83	84	85	86	87	88	89	90
91	92	93	94	95	96	97	98	99	100

Fill in the missing numbers in the threes pattern.

3   12   18   27

Note for parent: Notice that an odd number multiplied by an odd number = an odd number.
An odd number multiplied by an even number = an even number.

175

Multiplying by 4

Count by fours. Color in the fours pattern in the number square.

1	2	3	4	5	6	7	8	9	10
11	12	13	14	15	16	17	18	19	20
21	22	23	24	25	26	27	28	29	30
31	32	33	34	35	36	37	38	39	40
41	42	43	44	45	46	47	48	49	50
51	52	53	54	55	56	57	58	59	60
61	62	63	64	65	66	67	68	69	70
71	72	73	74	75	76	77	78	79	80
81	82	83	84	85	86	87	88	89	90
91	92	93	94	95	96	97	98	99	100

Fill in the missing numbers in the fours pattern.

4   12   20   32   40

Note for parent: Compare the pattern of the twos and fours in the number squares. All are even numbers and the products of the fours table appear in the twos table as well.

Multiplying by 5

Count by fives. Color in the fives pattern in the number square.

1	2	3	4	5	6	7	8	9	10
11	12	13	14	15	16	17	18	19	20
21	22	23	24	25	26	27	28	29	30
31	32	33	34	35	36	37	38	39	40
41	42	43	44	45	46	47	48	49	50
51	52	53	54	55	56	57	58	59	60
61	62	63	64	65	66	67	68	69	70
71	72	73	74	75	76	77	78	79	80
81	82	83	84	85	86	87	88	89	90
91	92	93	94	95	96	97	98	99	100

Fill in the missing numbers in the fives pattern.

5   20   30   50

Note for parent: Help your child to learn to count fluently by fives up to 100. Notice that in the fives pattern the ones digits in each number alternate: 5 0 5 0 5 0, etc.

Multiplying by 6

Count by sixes. Color in the sixes pattern in the number square.

1	2	3	4	5	6	7	8	9	10
11	12	13	14	15	16	17	18	19	20
21	22	23	24	25	26	27	28	29	30
31	32	33	34	35	36	37	38	39	40
41	42	43	44	45	46	47	48	49	50
51	52	53	54	55	56	57	58	59	60
61	62	63	64	65	66	67	68	69	70
71	72	73	74	75	76	77	78	79	80
81	82	83	84	85	86	87	88	89	90
91	92	93	94	95	96	97	98	99	100

Fill in the missing numbers in the sixes pattern.

6   24   36   54

Note for parent: Point out that all the multiples of 6 are even numbers, and if you look back a few pages you can see that they also appear in the threes number square.

Multiplying by 7

Count by sevens. Color in the sevens pattern in the number square.

1	2	3	4	5	6	7	8	9	10
11	12	13	14	15	16	17	18	19	20
21	22	23	24	25	26	27	28	29	30
31	32	33	34	35	36	37	38	39	40
41	42	43	44	45	46	47	48	49	50
51	52	53	54	55	56	57	58	59	60
61	62	63	64	65	66	67	68	69	70
71	72	73	74	75	76	77	78	79	80
81	82	83	84	85	86	87	88	89	90
91	92	93	94	95	96	97	98	99	100

Fill in the missing numbers in the sevens pattern.

7   28   42   56 63

Note for parent: Remember, even number x odd number = even number (2 x 7 = 14).
And odd number x odd number = odd number (3 x 7 = 21).

179

Multiplying by 8

Count by eights. Color in the eights pattern in the number square.

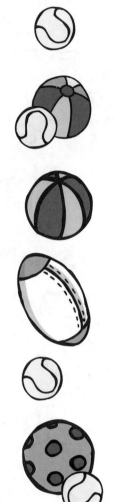
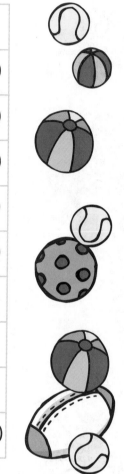

1	2	3	4	5	6	7	8	9	10
11	12	13	14	15	16	17	18	19	20
21	22	23	24	25	26	27	28	29	30
31	32	33	34	35	36	37	38	39	40
41	42	43	44	45	46	47	48	49	50
51	52	53	54	55	56	57	58	59	60
61	62	63	64	65	66	67	68	69	70
71	72	73	74	75	76	77	78	79	80
81	82	83	84	85	86	87	88	89	90
91	92	93	94	95	96	97	98	99	100

Fill in the missing numbers in the eights pattern.

8   32   48   56   72

Note for parent: Multiples of 8 (i.e. 08, 16, 24, 32, 40, 48, 56, 64, 72, 80) have tens digits that increase by one: 0, 1, 2, 3, 4, 4, 5, 6, 7, 8. Except the 4, which is repeated!

Multiplying by 9

Count by nines. Color in the nines pattern in the number square.

1	2	3	4	5	6	7	8	9	10
11	12	13	14	15	16	17	18	19	20
21	22	23	24	25	26	27	28	29	30
31	32	33	34	35	36	37	38	39	40
41	42	43	44	45	46	47	48	49	50
51	52	53	54	55	56	57	58	59	60
61	62	63	64	65	66	67	68	69	70
71	72	73	74	75	76	77	78	79	80
81	82	83	84	85	86	87	88	89	90
91	92	93	94	95	96	97	98	99	100

Fill in the missing numbers in the nines pattern.

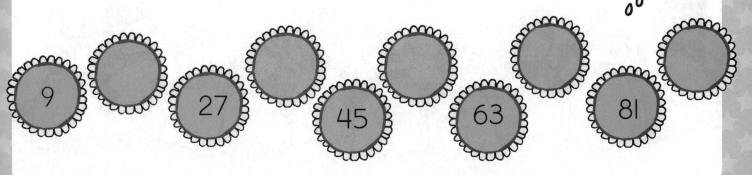

9   27   45   63   81

Note for parent: Multiples of 9 (i.e. 09, 18, 27, 36) have digits that add up to 9 (0 + 9, 1 + 8, 2 + 7, 3 + 6, etc.)! When you reach 99, add the digits 9 + 9 = 18 and 1 + 8 = 9.

181

Multiplying by 10

Count by tens. Color in the tens pattern in the number square.

1	2	3	4	5	6	7	8	9	10
11	12	13	14	15	16	17	18	19	20
21	22	23	24	25	26	27	28	29	30
31	32	33	34	35	36	37	38	39	40
41	42	43	44	45	46	47	48	49	50
51	52	53	54	55	56	57	58	59	60
61	62	63	64	65	66	67	68	69	70
71	72	73	74	75	76	77	78	79	80
81	82	83	84	85	86	87	88	89	90
91	92	93	94	95	96	97	98	99	100

Fill in the missing numbers in the tens pattern.

10   50   90

Note for parent: Help your child to learn to count fluently by tens up to 1,000. Only the tens digit changes, as you would expect because you are counting by tens.

Multiplication Chart

Fill in the numbers to complete the multiplication chart.

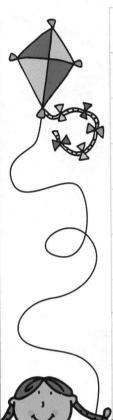

0	1	2	3	4	5	6	7	8	9	10
1	1	2	3	4	5	6				10
2	2	4	6	8	10	12	14	16	18	
3	3	6	9	12	15	18				
4	4	8	12	16	20	24				
5	5	10	15	20	25	30	35		50	
6	6	12	18	24	30	36		54		
7	7	14	21	28	35	42	49			70
8	8	16	24	32	40					
9	9	18	27	36	45	54		81		
10	10	20	30	40	50	60	70	80	90	100

You can use the multiplication chart to help you answer these questions.

$7 \times 6 = 42$ $8 \times 4 = 32$ $9 \times 3 = 27$

$8 \times 9 = 72$ $5 \times 5 = 25$ $8 \times 8 = 64$

Note for parent: Help your child to learn to recite the multiplication tables from 1 to 10. This knowledge will help them to work out calculations much faster.

183

Multiplication Problems

Figure out the answers to these word problems by multiplying.

1. Jon has 6 stickers. Jake has double this amount.

How many stickers does Jake have?

....

2. How many days are in 7 weeks? ....

3. If Annie saves $3 a week for 4 weeks, how many dollars

does she have? ....

4. There are 8 children in a group. They each have 4 books.

How many books altogether? ....

5. There are 9 children at a party. They eat 3 cupcakes each.

How many cupcakes do they eat altogether? ....

6. There are 5 monkeys at the zoo. They eat 6 bananas each!

How many bananas do they eat altogether? ....

Note for parent: Encourage your child to try to figure out the answers mentally. If this is too difficult, use the space on the page for your work.

Multilication with Larger Numbers

If you need to multiply larger numbers, it helps to split the number up into tens and ones. Like this:

$$26 \times 3 = (20 \times 3) + (6 \times 3)$$
$$= 60 \; + \; 18$$
$$= 78$$

Try this way of working to solve these equations.

$14 \times 7 = (10 \times 7) + (4 \times 7)$

= ....

= ....

$22 \times 4 = (20 \times 4) + (2 \times 4)$

= ....

= ....

$32 \times 5 = (30 \times 5) + (2 \times 5)$

= ....

= ....

$47 \times 3 = (40 \times 3) + (7 \times 3)$

= ....

= ....

$51 \times 9 = (50 \times 9) + (1 \times 9)$

= ....

= ....

$62 \times 2 = (60 \times 2) + (2 \times 2)$

= ....

= ....

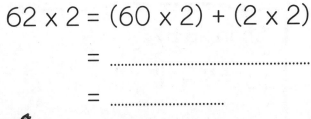

Note for parent: When we multiply two numbers together, we get the product of those numbers.

185

Division and Sharing

Division is like sharing equally.

> 12 stickers shared between 4 children is:
> $12 \div 4 = 3$
> The children get 3 star stickers each.

Complete these division sums by sharing.

Share 18 by 3

$18 \div 3 =$ ☐

Share 9 by 3

$9 \div 3 =$ ☐

Share 12 by 6

$12 \div 6 =$ ☐

Share 16 by 4

$16 \div 4 =$ ☐

Share 18 by 9

$18 \div 9 =$ ☐

Share 20 by 4

$20 \div 4 =$ ☐

Note for parent: Think about the different ways in which a collection of objects can be shared equally, for example: with 12 objects $12 \div 12 = 1$, $12 \div 6 = 2$, $12 \div 2 = 6$, $12 \div 4 = 3$, $12 \div 3 = 4$.

Division on a Number Line

You can solve division questions by using a number line.

Think about 10 ÷ 2 as "how many 2s make 10?,"
and count in twos on a number line.

0   2   4   6   8   10

There are 5 hops of 2 to reach 10.   10 ÷ 2 = 5

Solve these division questions using a number line.

20 ÷ 4 = ☐

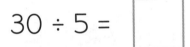

0   4   20

30 ÷ 5 = ☐

0   5   30

36 ÷ 6 = ☐

0   6   36

Note for parent: Using the number line in this way helps children to see the connection
between repeated addition, multiplication, and division.

187

Division Problems

Figure out the answers to these word problems by dividing.

1. How many lengths of 5 inches can you cut

from 20 inches of string? ....

2. Sixteen children are running in a relay race.

The teacher divides them into 4 equal teams.

How many children are in each team? ....

3. In a pattern of 12 tiles, every third tile is red.

How many red tiles are there? ....

4. Share 25 bones equally between 8 dogs.

How many bones are left over? ....

5. Divide 20 balloons equally between 3 clowns.

How many balloons each? ....

How many are left over? ....

6. Kim walks the same distance every day.

She walks 21 miles in a week.

How many miles does she walk each day? ....

Note for parent: Encourage your child to use their knowledge of multiplication facts in reverse to find the answers to these division problems.

Division and Multiplication

Division is the opposite of multiplication.

If you know that 5 x 3 = 15, then you also know that:

$$15 \div 3 = 5 \qquad 15 \div 5 = 3$$

Complete two division facts for each equation.

3 x 4 = 12

12 ÷ 4 = 3

12 ÷ 3 = 4

25 x 3 = 75

75 ÷ 3 = 25

75 ÷ 25 = 3

15 x 2 = 30

30 ÷ 2 = 15

30 ÷ 15 = 2

50 x 2 = 100

100 ÷ 2 = 50

100 ÷ 50 = 2

20 x 3 = 60

60 ÷ 3 = 20

60 ÷ 20 = 3

50 x 4 = 200

200 ÷ 4 = 50

200 ÷ 50 = 4

Note for parent: Once your child has a firm grasp of Multiplication facts, then division will become easier.

189

Number Puzzle

Solve this number puzzle using your multiplication and division skills.

Across

1. Double 23

3. Fifty multiplied by 4

6. 5 groups of 7

7. 9 times 9

9. 15 ÷ 5, multiplied by 6

10. Three 50s

Down

2. Six times ten

3. 100 divided by 4

4. Nine groups of 10

5. 7 x 4

8. How many fives in 45?

9. 100 ÷ 10

Note for parent: This puzzle uses written questions phrased in a variety of ways to provide practice in the language of multiplication and division.

Alligator Attack

To escape the alligators, you must cross the river by jumping on boulders. You can only land on a boulder that will divide evenly by three. Color in the boulders you can safely land on.

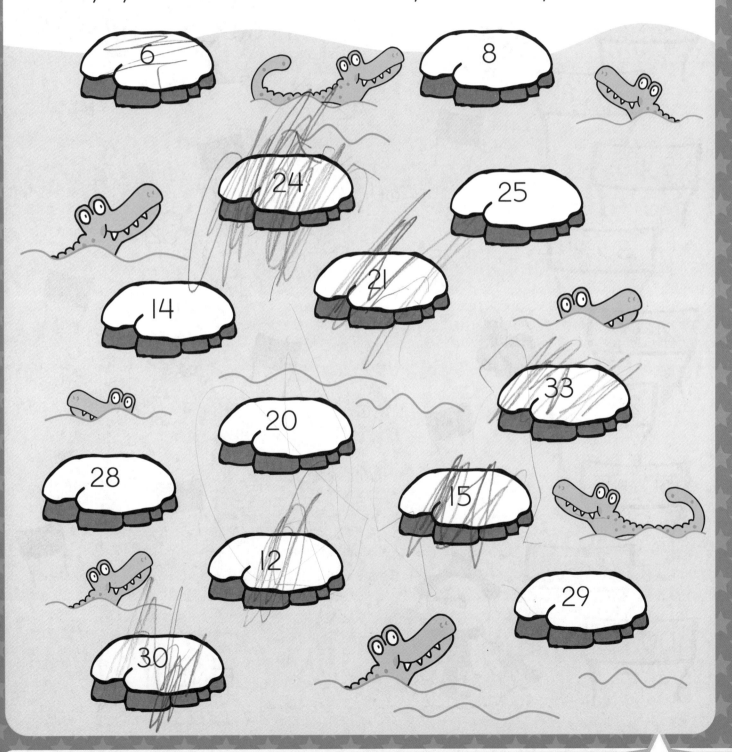

Note for parent: Your child needs to find multiples of 3 to cross the river. This activity will provide practice in counting by threes and dividing by 3.

Slalom Ski Race

Find the correct path through the slalom to win the race! The answers to these sums mark the route.

6 x 7

8 x 8

5 x 6

3 x 9

21 ÷ 7

24 ÷ 3

50 ÷ 5

49 ÷ 7

100 ÷ 5

42

44

64

4

35

30

32

9

27

6

3

16

10

8

7

40

44

73

20

FINISH

Note for parent: This activity provides practice in quick recall of multiplication and division facts.

Math Machine

Divide the numbers going into the machine. Write the numbers coming out in the boxes.

40 → in → out → 10

24 → 6

36 → 9

16 → 4

28 → 7

÷ 4

Note for parent: This activity provides practice in quick recall of the products and factors of four.

Division Equations

Fill in the missing numbers to make each total the same.
The first one has been done for you.

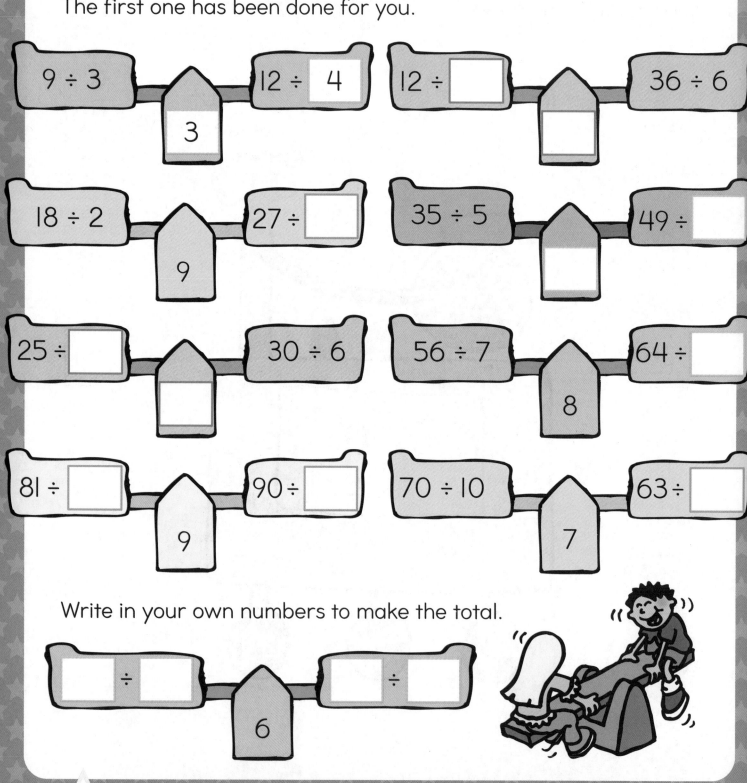

$9 \div 3$ 3 $12 \div 4$ $12 \div \boxed{}$ $\boxed{}$ $36 \div 6$

$18 \div 2$ 9 $27 \div \boxed{}$ $35 \div 5$ $\boxed{}$ $49 \div \boxed{}$

$25 \div \boxed{}$ $\boxed{}$ $30 \div 6$ $56 \div 7$ 8 $64 \div \boxed{}$

$81 \div \boxed{}$ 9 $90 \div \boxed{}$ $70 \div 10$ 7 $63 \div \boxed{}$

Write in your own numbers to make the total.

$\boxed{} \div \boxed{}$ 6 $\boxed{} \div \boxed{}$

Note for parent: Remind your child of what is meant by "factors" and "product." For example, 12 is the product of 6 x 2, and 6 and 2 are factors of 12.

Mixed Equations

Fill in the missing numbers to make each total. The first one has been done for you.

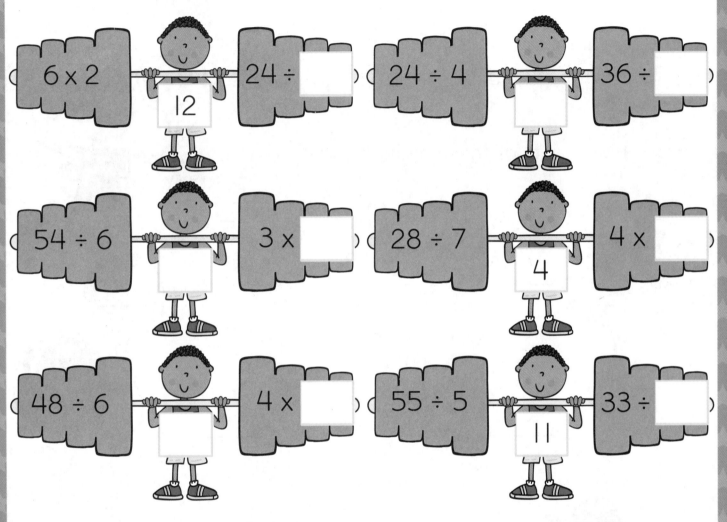

6 x 2 | 12 | 24 ÷ ☐

24 ÷ 4 | ☐ | 36 ÷ ☐

54 ÷ 6 | ☐ | 3 x ☐

28 ÷ 7 | 4 | 4 x ☐

48 ÷ 6 | ☐ | 4 x ☐

55 ÷ 5 | 11 | 33 ÷ ☐

Write in your own numbers to make the total.

☐ x ☐ | 12 | ☐ ÷ ☐

Note for parent: This activity provides more practice with equations and quick recall of multiplication and division facts.

Long Multiplication

Sometimes it is easier to multiply 2-digit numbers in columns, like this:

Multiply the ones first.
Then multiply the tens.

$$\begin{array}{r} 1\ 2 \\ \times\ \ 4 \\ \hline 4\ 8 \end{array}$$

Find the product of these multiplications.

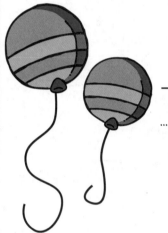

$$\begin{array}{r} 3\ 3 \\ \times\ 3 \\ \hline \end{array}$$

$$\begin{array}{r} 4\ 1 \\ \times\ 8 \\ \hline \end{array}$$

$$\begin{array}{r} 5\ 9 \\ \times\ 1 \\ \hline \end{array}$$

$$\begin{array}{r} 6\ 2 \\ \times\ 3 \\ \hline \end{array}$$

$$\begin{array}{r} 7\ 4 \\ \times\ 2 \\ \hline \end{array}$$

$$\begin{array}{r} 6\ 1 \\ \times\ 5 \\ \hline \end{array}$$

$$\begin{array}{r} 8\ 0 \\ \times\ 4 \\ \hline \end{array}$$

$$\begin{array}{r} 3\ 1 \\ \times\ 9 \\ \hline \end{array}$$

Note for parent: Show your child where to start. Point to the ones digits in the column on the right. Multiply the ones and write the answer. Then multiply the tens.

Long Multiplication with Regrouping

Find the product of these multiplications. Multiply the ones first. If this makes 10, or more, you need to regroup. Next, multiply the tens and add the number you carried over.

```
  2
  2 6
x   4
-----
1 0 4
```

Find the answer to these multiplications. You will need to regroup.

```
  1 8        3 4        5 5
x   4      x   4      x   5
-----      -----      -----

```

```
  7 7        8 9        3 4
x   3      x   3      x   5
-----      -----      -----

```

```
  5 6        9 7        4 6
x   6      x   4      x   3
-----      -----      -----

```

Long Division

Sometimes it is easier to divide 2-digit numbers when we write them like this:

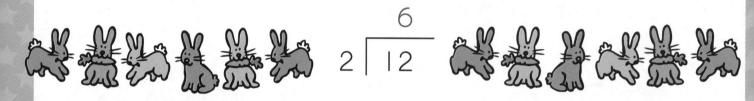

$$2\overline{)12} = 6$$

Work out how many 2s are in 12 and write the answer above.
Now try these:

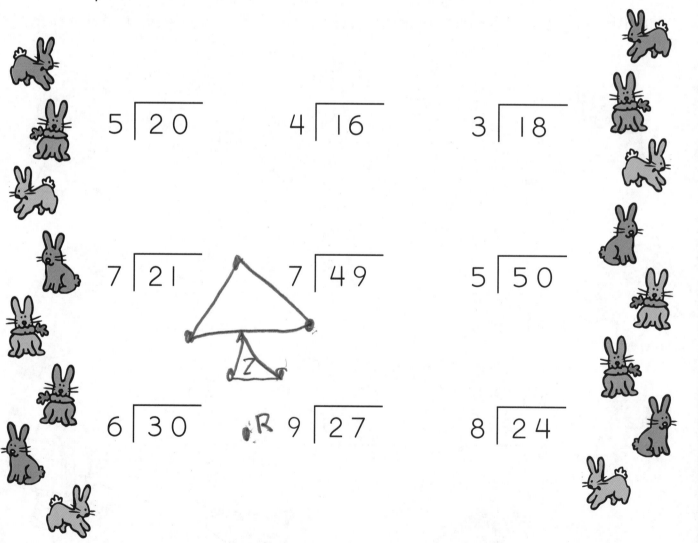

$$5\overline{)20} \qquad 4\overline{)16} \qquad 3\overline{)18}$$

$$7\overline{)21} \qquad 7\overline{)49} \qquad 5\overline{)50}$$

$$6\overline{)30} \qquad 9\overline{)27} \qquad 8\overline{)24}$$

Note for parent: This activity provides practice in quick recall of multiplication and division facts.

Long Division with Remainders

Some numbers don't divide equally.

For example: If you wanted to divide 13 cookies equally onto 2 plates, you could put 6 cookies on each plate and have one cookie left over.

This one cookie leftover is called a remainder. It is written as "r" for short.

$$2\overline{)13} \quad 6 \; r1$$

Now try these:

$$5\overline{)22} \qquad 4\overline{)25} \qquad 3\overline{)23}$$

$$6\overline{)19} \qquad 7\overline{)17} \qquad 8\overline{)33}$$

$$5\overline{)34} \qquad 6\overline{)37} \qquad 9\overline{)28}$$

Two-Step Word Problems

With each of these word problems, you must do two separate calculations to find the answer.

1. There are 4 red balls and 3 blue balls in a net. How many balls in 5 nets?

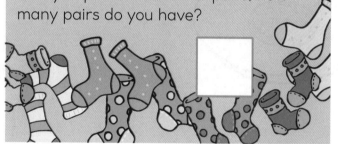

2. Ten children are on a bus. 8 more get on and 3 get off. How many children are on the bus now?

3. If you put 24 socks into pairs, how many pairs do you have?

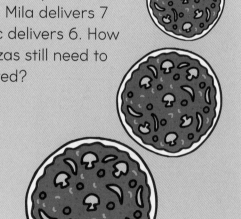

4. There are 12 books on the top shelf and 10 books on the bottom shelf. 15 books are removed. How many books are left on the shelves?

5. There are 18 pizzas to be delivered. Mila delivers 7 and Isaac delivers 6. How many pizzas still need to be delivered?

6. There are 25 children at a party and 51 cupcakes. How many cupcakes does each child get?

How many are left over?

Note for parent: Your child will use four math skills: addition, subtraction, multiplication, and division to solve these problems.

Number Trail

Follow the number trail to the end. Figure out the answer to a question, then use the answer to figure out the next question. Write your answers in the spaces.

10 × 2 = 20 × 5 = 100 ÷

8 × 5 = 5 ÷ 25 = 4

= 40 ÷ 10 = 4 × 12 =

48 ÷ 8 = 5 ÷

Note for parent: This activity requires quick recall of multiplication and division facts.

201

Magic Squares

In this magic square, the numbers going across, down the sides, and diagonally add up to the same amount: 15.

4	9	2	= 15
3	5	7	= 15
8	1	6	= 15
=	=	=	
15	15	15	

Figure out the missing numbers to complete the magic squares.

10	3	8
5	7	9
6	11	4

= 21

5		7
	8	
9		11

= 24

10		12
	9	7
	13	

= 27

12	7	
		9
8		10

= 33

Note for parent: This activity provides practice in mental math and the quick recall of addition and subtraction facts.

Pyramid Puzzles

Solve these pyramid puzzles. Figure out the missing numbers in the upper layer of bricks by multiplying the two bricks underneath. The first one is done for you.

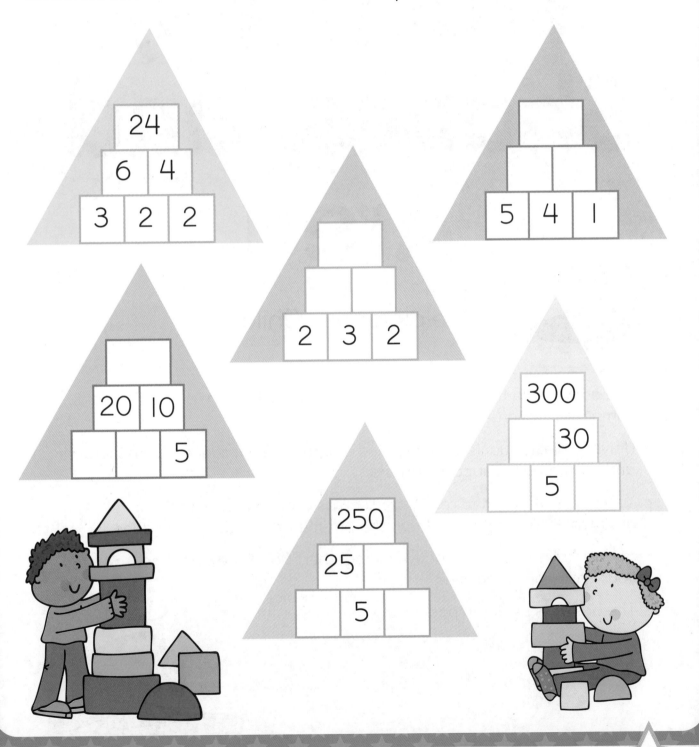

Note for parent: This activity provides practice in mental math and the quick recall of multiplication and division facts.

203

Fractions, Shapes, and Area

Helping Your Child

- The activities in this section will help your child to learn about fractions, compare fractions, and find equivalents.

- Halves, thirds, quarters, sixths, and eighths are introduced, with pictures and diagrams to support learning.

- Your child will learn to recognize regular 2-dimensional and 3-dimensional shapes, and find the perimeter and area of shapes.

- Set aside time to do the activities together. Do a little at a time, so that your child enjoys learning.

- The answers begin on page 316.

Contents

Fractions

A **fraction** is an equal part of something. We can divide this pizza into 2 equal parts, or 2 **halves**.

We can divide it in half in lots of other ways, too!

Two halves are written as $\frac{2}{2}$.

Draw 4 different ways of dividing these shapes into equal halves. You can use a ruler if you prefer.

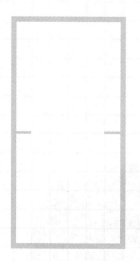   

2 halves = $\frac{2}{2}$ 2 halves = $\frac{2}{2}$ 2 halves = $\frac{2}{2}$ 2 halves = $\frac{2}{2}$

Note for parent: This activity will help children to recognize what is meant by one half, and that 2 halves make a whole one.

Halves

If you eat half of the pizza,
you eat one part out of 2 parts.

We write this as $\frac{1}{2}$.

Color one half of each shape.

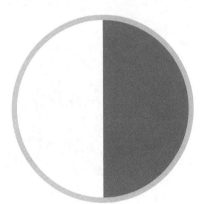

one half = $\frac{1}{2}$

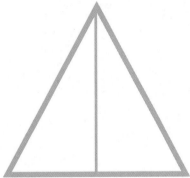

one half = $\frac{1}{2}$

one half = $\frac{1}{2}$

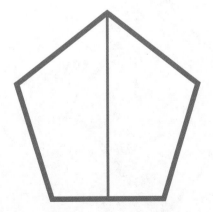

one half = $\frac{1}{2}$

one half = $\frac{1}{2}$

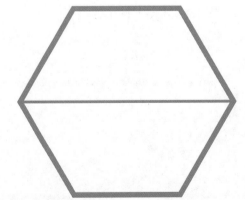

one half = $\frac{1}{2}$

Note for parent: You can demonstrate the concept of dividing a whole object into halves using cakes, cookies, or pizza.

207

Quarters

If we divide a pizza into halves and then half again, we get 4 **quarters**.

4 quarters = $\frac{4}{4}$

If we color one part out of 4, this is $\frac{1}{4}$.

Divide these shapes into 4 quarters. Then color one quarter of each shape.

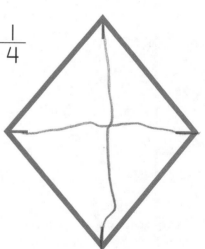

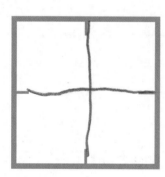

one quarter = $\frac{1}{4}$

one quarter = $\frac{1}{4}$

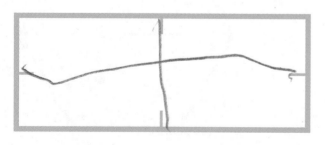

one quarter = $\frac{1}{4}$

one quarter = $\frac{1}{4}$

Note for parent: We can explain fractions as being like division. We are dividing a whole one into equal parts. We write $\frac{1}{4}$ because this is a whole one divided by 4.

Thirds

When we divide something into 3 equal parts, we get **thirds**.

3 thirds = $\frac{3}{3}$

If we color one part out of 3, this is $\frac{1}{3}$.

Color one third of each shape.

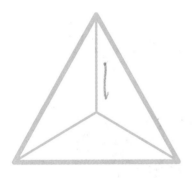

one third = $\frac{1}{3}$

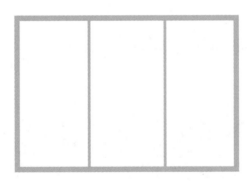

one third = $\frac{1}{3}$

one third = $\frac{1}{3}$

Color one third of the cookies in the box.
You could draw lines to divide the box into thirds first.

Note for parent: Children need to learn that to find one half they divide by 2, to find one third they divide by 3, and to find one quarter they divide by 4, etc.

209

Fractions of Numbers

We can find a fraction of a group of objects by dividing the group into equal parts. This is like sharing.

Count and circle **one half** of the apples.

$\frac{1}{2}$ of 12 = ☐

Count and circle **one quarter** of the ice cream cones.

$\frac{1}{4}$ of 12 = ☐

Count and circle **one third** of the drinks.

$\frac{1}{3}$ of 12 = ☐

Note for parent: You can practice this activity using collections of small objects or toys found in the home such as socks, shells, marbles, and buttons.

More Fractions of Numbers

Complete the fraction sentences.

Share 9 balloons so that each child gets $\frac{1}{3}$.

$\frac{1}{3}$ of $\boxed{9}$ = $\boxed{3}$

Each child gets $\boxed{}$ balloons.

Share 12 leaves so that each caterpillar gets $\frac{1}{6}$.

$\frac{1}{6}$ of $\boxed{}$ = $\boxed{}$

Each caterpillar gets $\boxed{}$ leaves.

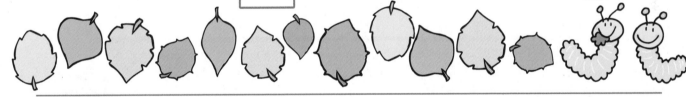

Share 8 carrots so that each rabbit gets $\frac{1}{8}$.

$\frac{1}{8}$ of $\boxed{}$ = $\boxed{}$

Each rabbit gets $\boxed{}$ carrot.

Note for parent: This activity demonstrates how division and fractions are related.

211

Fraction Bars

Color one half, $\frac{1}{2}$.

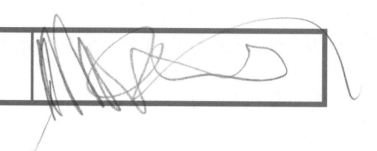

Color two quarters, $\frac{2}{4}$.

Color four eighths, $\frac{4}{8}$.

What do you notice about the parts you have colored?
Complete the fraction equation:

$$\frac{1}{2} = \frac{2}{4} = \boxed{}$$

Fraction Wall

Color these fractions in the wall below: $\frac{1}{2}$, $\frac{2}{4}$, $\frac{4}{8}$, $\frac{1}{3}$, and $\frac{2}{6}$.

halves

thirds

quarters

sixths

eighths

Compare the fractions in size.
Write the correct signs in between the fractions.
Use the fraction wall to help you.

$\frac{1}{2}$ [>] $\frac{1}{3}$ $\frac{1}{2}$ [ ] $\frac{2}{4}$

$\frac{1}{2}$ [ ] $\frac{3}{6}$ $\frac{1}{3}$ [>] $\frac{2}{3}$

$\frac{1}{4}$ [ ] $\frac{1}{8}$ $\frac{1}{4}$ [ ] $\frac{2}{8}$

$\frac{1}{2}$ [ ] $\frac{4}{8}$ $\frac{2}{6}$ [ ] $\frac{4}{8}$

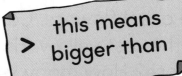
> this means bigger than

< this means less than

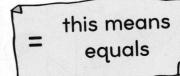
= this means equals

Note for parent: Children can use fraction bars and walls to help them visualize and compare different fractions.

Fraction Problems

If I eat $\frac{1}{3}$ of this chocolate bar, how many pieces are left?

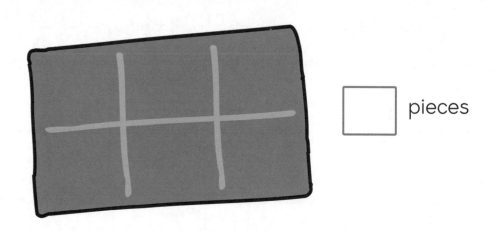

☐ pieces

If I eat $\frac{1}{4}$ of these candies, how many are left?

☐ candies

There are 9 flowers. Color $\frac{1}{3}$ of them red and color the rest yellow. How many red flowers are there? How many yellow flowers?

☐ red flowers

☐ yellow flowers

Note for parent: This activity helps practice logic and reasoning skills, as well as knowledge of fractions. Your child can use the illustrations to help solve the problems.

More Fraction Problems

Read the questions and write how many animals there are altogether.

How many parrots are there altogether if this is $\frac{1}{2}$ of them?

☐ parrots altogether

How many seagulls are there altogether if this is $\frac{1}{4}$ of them?

☐ seagulls altogether

How many penguins are there altogether if this is $\frac{1}{6}$ of them?

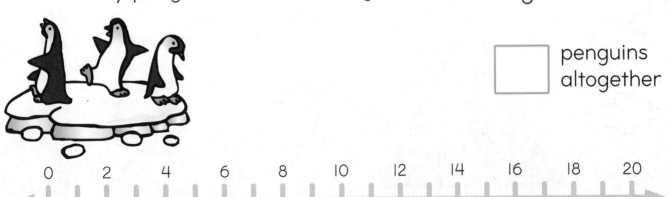

☐ penguins altogether

0 2 4 6 8 10 12 14 16 18 20

Note for parent: Your child will need to count or multiply to get the number of animals altogether.

215

Circle the Fraction

Circle the correct fraction. Count the number of parts in the whole to find the bottom number and the shaded parts to find the top number.

$\frac{1}{2}$ $\qquad$ $\frac{3}{3}$ $\qquad$ $\frac{3}{4}$

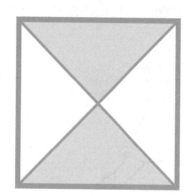

$\frac{2}{3}$ $\qquad$ $\frac{2}{4}$ $\qquad$ $\frac{1}{4}$

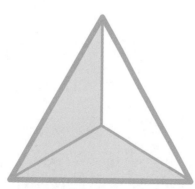

$\frac{1}{2}$ $\qquad$ $\frac{1}{3}$ $\qquad$ $\frac{2}{3}$

Note for parent: The bottom number is called the denominator and the top number is called the numerator.

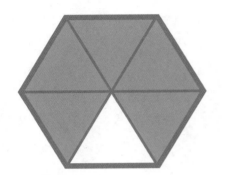
$$\frac{5}{6} \qquad \frac{4}{6} \qquad \frac{3}{4}$$

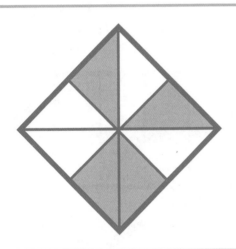
$$\frac{4}{6} \qquad \frac{4}{8} \qquad \frac{3}{4}$$

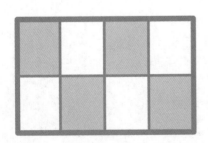
$$\frac{4}{8} \qquad \frac{4}{6} \qquad \frac{4}{4}$$

Write the Fraction

What fraction of these shapes is shaded?
Write the fraction next to each shape. The first one is done for you.

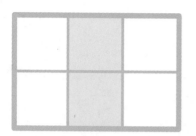

$$\frac{2}{6}$$

This fraction means that 2 parts out of 6 parts are shaded.

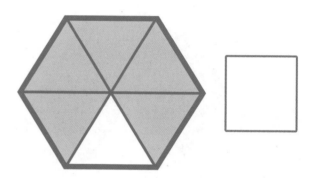

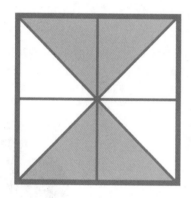

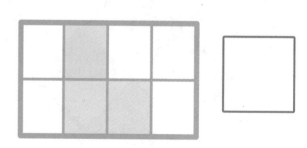

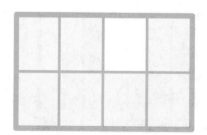

Note for parent: The top number tells us how many parts there are altogether. The bottom number is the number of parts we are looking at.

Color the Fraction

Color each fraction of the circle to match the label below.

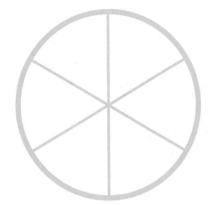

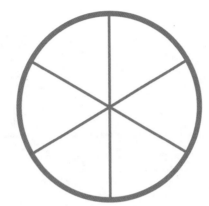

$\dfrac{1}{6}$

$\dfrac{2}{6}$

$\dfrac{3}{6}$

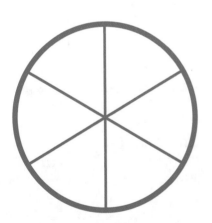

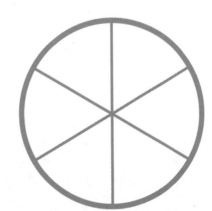

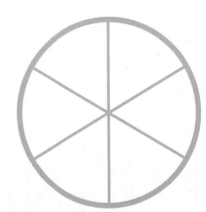

$\dfrac{4}{6}$

$\dfrac{5}{6}$

$\dfrac{6}{6} = 1$

Note for parent: It is important for children to understand that $\frac{2}{2} = 1$, $\frac{3}{3} = 1$, $\frac{4}{4} = 1$, $\frac{6}{6} = 1$, $\frac{8}{8} = 1$, and so on.

Number Line Fractions

Fill in the missing fractions on the number lines.
The first one is done for you.

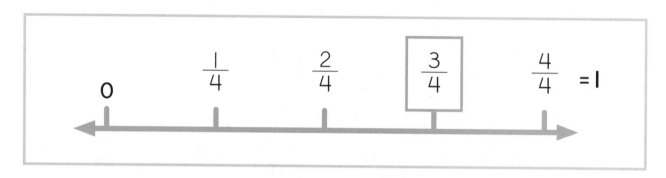

$\frac{1}{4}$ $\frac{2}{4}$ $\boxed{\frac{3}{4}}$ $\frac{4}{4}$ = 1

0

0   $\frac{2}{3}$ = 1

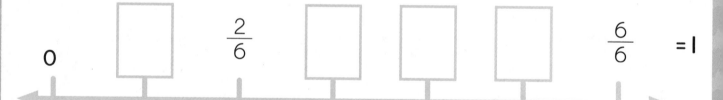

0   $\frac{2}{6}$ $\frac{6}{6}$ = 1

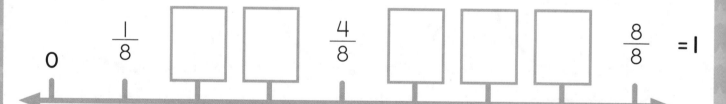

0   $\frac{1}{8}$ $\frac{4}{8}$ $\frac{8}{8}$ = 1

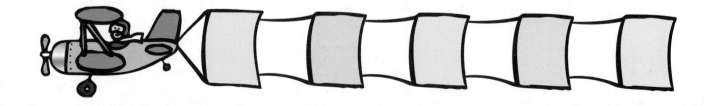

Note for parent: Children can draw simple number lines like this to help them visualize, compare, and order fractions by size.

More Number Line Fractions

Write these fractions in the correct place on the number line.
The first one is done for you.

| $\frac{1}{2}$ | $\frac{1}{4}$ | $\frac{3}{4}$ |

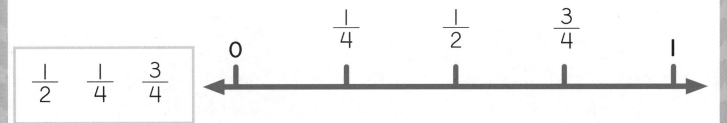

| $\frac{4}{8}$ | $\frac{1}{8}$ | $\frac{6}{8}$ |

| $\frac{1}{3}$ | $\frac{2}{3}$ |

| $\frac{5}{6}$ | $\frac{1}{2}$ | $\frac{1}{6}$ |

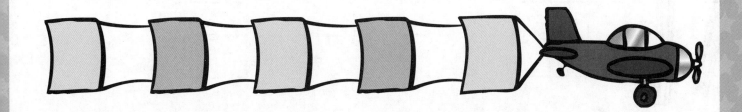

Note for parent: This activity reviews important concepts, for example, $\frac{1}{2} = \frac{2}{4} = \frac{4}{8} = \frac{3}{6}$.

221

Equivalent Fractions

Color the fractions that are equal in size.
The first one is done for you.

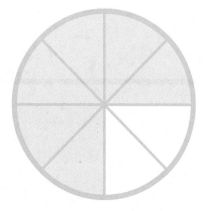

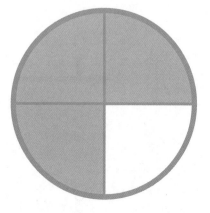

$$\boxed{\frac{6}{8}} \quad = \quad \boxed{\frac{3}{4}}$$

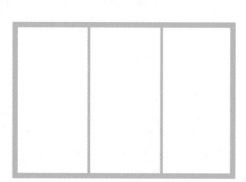

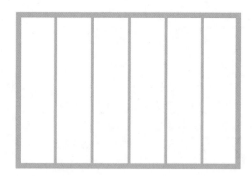

$$\boxed{\frac{1}{3}} \quad = \quad \boxed{\frac{2}{6}}$$

Note for parent: Two fractions are equivalent if they are the same size. This activity reviews important concepts, for example, $\frac{1}{2} = \frac{2}{4} = \frac{4}{8} = \frac{3}{6}$.

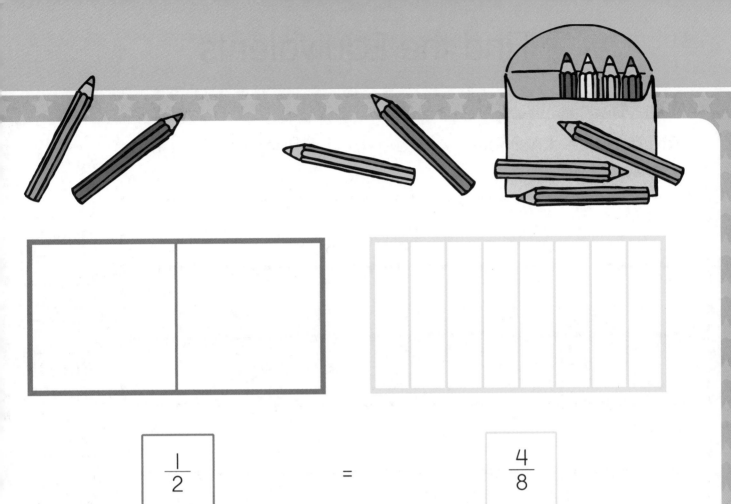

$$\frac{1}{2} \qquad = \qquad \frac{4}{8}$$

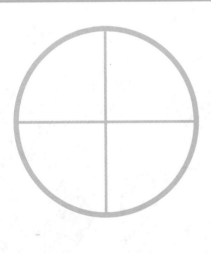

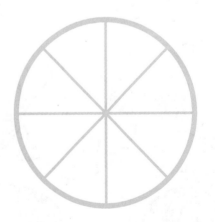

$$\frac{1}{4} \qquad = \qquad \frac{2}{8}$$

Find the Equivalents

You can use a number wall to help you find fractions that are equal in size.

halves

thirds

quarters

sixths

eighths

Draw lines to join the fractions that are equal.

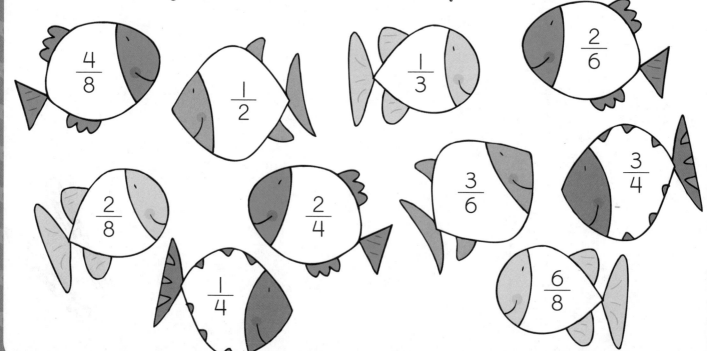

Note for parent: The number wall will help your child to compare and visualize equivalent fractions.

Reasoning about Fractions

Write the missing sign **>** or **<** in between the fractions.

Which is more? One quarter of a ribbon, or one half?
Estimate first, then color the fractions to find out.

$\frac{1}{4}$ ☐ $\frac{1}{2}$

Which is more? One quarter of a big bar of chocolate,
or one half of a small bar?

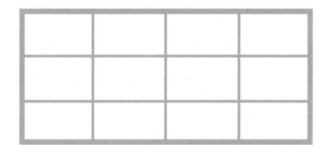 

$\frac{1}{4}$ of 12 = ☐ pieces ☐ $\frac{1}{2}$ of 4 = ☐ pieces

Which is more? One half of the paint
in a 2-pint tin, or one third of the
paint in a 9-pint tin?

$\frac{1}{2}$ of 2 pints = ☐ pint ☐ $\frac{1}{3}$ of 9 pints = ☐ pints

Fractions of Numbers

Use the number lines to work out these fractions.

$\frac{1}{4}$ of 20 = ☐

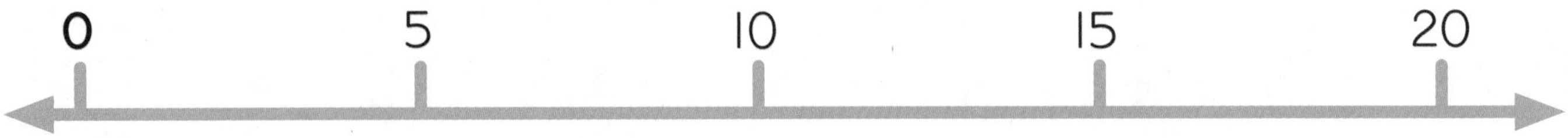

0   5   10   15   20

$\frac{1}{4}$ of 24 = ☐

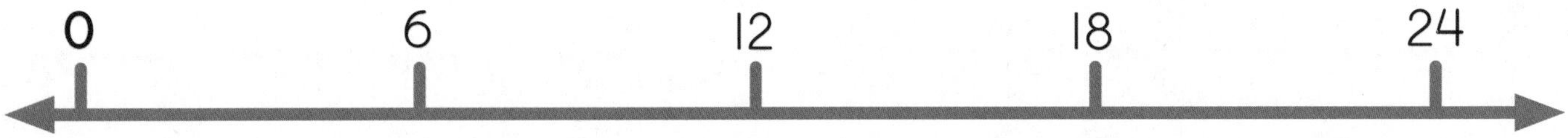

0   6   12   18   24

$\frac{1}{3}$ of 21 = ☐

0   7   14   21

$\frac{1}{6}$ of 24 = ☐

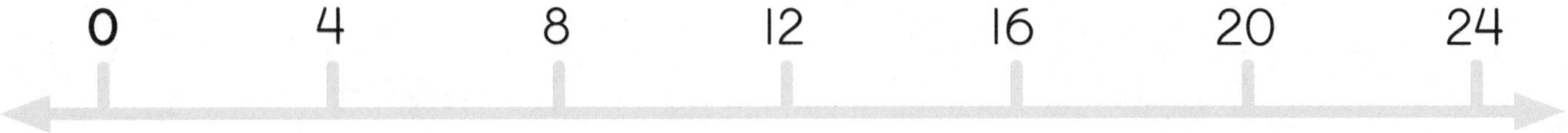

0   4   8   12   16   20   24

Note for parent: Using these number lines like a ruler, your child can find fractions by dividing the line.

Fractions and Division

Fractions are like division.

For example:

$\frac{1}{2}$ of 12 = 6   because   12 ÷ 2 = 6

Find these fractions by dividing.

$\frac{1}{3}$ of 15 =

15 ÷ 3 = ☐

$\frac{1}{3}$ of 30 =

30 ÷ 3 = ☐

$\frac{1}{6}$ of 18 =

18 ÷ 6 = ☐

$\frac{1}{6}$ of 36 =

36 ÷ 6 = ☐

$\frac{1}{8}$ of 16 =

16 ÷ 8 = ☐

$\frac{1}{8}$ of 32 =

32 ÷ 8 = ☐

$\frac{1}{4}$ of 40 =

40 ÷ 4 = ☐

$\frac{1}{2}$ of 50 =

50 ÷ 2 = ☐

Note for parent: Encourage your child to find the answers using mental math and knowledge of multiplication and division facts.

227

Problems

Read the questions and write the fractions.

If $\frac{1}{4}$ of the rockets are red and the rest are white, what fraction are white?

$$\boxed{\frac{3}{4}}$$

If $\frac{1}{3}$ of the aliens come from Planet Zig and the rest are from Zag, what fraction are from Zag?

If $\frac{4}{6}$ of the aliens are friendly and the rest are not, what fraction are unfriendly?

If $\frac{3}{8}$ of the astronauts go on a space walk, what fraction do not go on a space walk?

Note for parent: This activity reviews fractions and problem-solving.

Figure out the answers to these fraction problems.

12 children were asked about their pets.

$\frac{1}{2}$ have a dog

$\frac{1}{3}$ have a cat

$\frac{1}{6}$ have a fish

Write the numbers.

$\frac{1}{2}$ of 12   is the same as $12 \div 2 =$ ☐

$\frac{1}{3}$ of 12   is the same as $12 \div 3 =$ ☐

$\frac{1}{6}$ of 12   is the same as $12 \div 6 =$ ☐

16 children were asked about their favorite ice cream flavors.

$\frac{1}{2}$ liked chocolate

$\frac{1}{4}$ liked strawberry

$\frac{1}{8}$ liked vanilla

$\frac{1}{8}$ liked mint

Write the numbers.

$\frac{1}{2}$ of 16   is the same as $16 \div 2 =$ ☐

$\frac{1}{4}$ of 16   is the same as $16 \div 4 =$ ☐

$\frac{1}{8}$ of 16   is the same as $16 \div 8 =$ ☐

Note for parent: This activity reviews fractions of numbers and how fractions are related to division.

Triangles

A flat shape with 3 straight sides and 3 angles (corners) is called a **triangle**.
Find and circle the triangles.

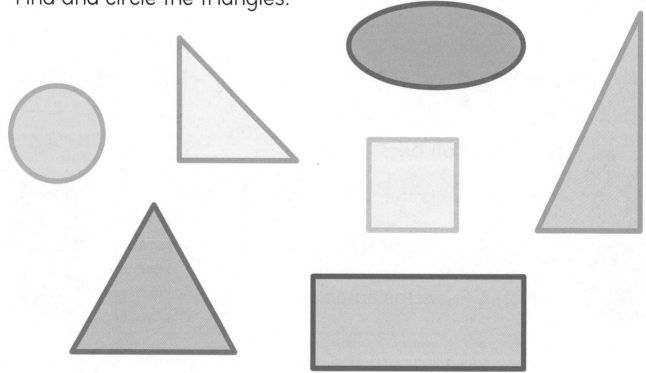

Color the triangles below using this key:

blue = a triangle with 3 equal sides

red = a triangle with 2 equal sides

green = a triangle with no equal sides

1.
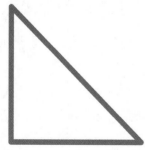

2.
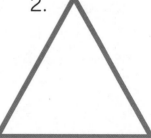

3.

Note for parent: Your child will need to look carefully to spot the differences between these triangles. The prefix tri in triangle means "three."

Quadrilaterals

A shape that has 4 straight sides and 4 angles is called a **quadrilateral**. These shapes are all quadrilaterals. Complete the descriptions by circling the correct words.

square

4 (equal) / **different** sides,

4 equal angles

rhombus

It looks like a diamond!

4 equal sides,

opposite angles are

equal / different

rectangle

4 equal angles,

opposite sides are

equal / different

What shape are these picture frames? Name them correctly.

1. ....

2. ....

3. ....

Note for parent: Help your child to remember what a quadrilateral is by pointing out that the prefix quad means "four."

231

More Quadrilaterals

These shapes are also quadrilaterals. Complete the descriptions by circling the correct words.

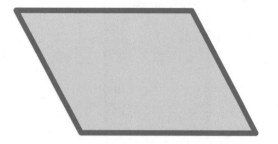

parallelogram

opposite sides are parallel and

opposite angles are **equal / different**

trapezoid

has **two / four** parallel sides

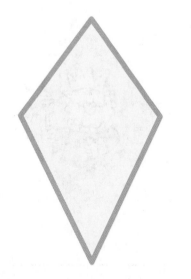

kite

the sides next to

each other are the

same / different length

Note for parent: Any four-sided shape with 4 straight sides and 4 angles is a quadrilateral.

Draw Quadrilaterals

Use this space to draw different kinds of quadrilaterals. Remember your shapes need to have 4 sides.

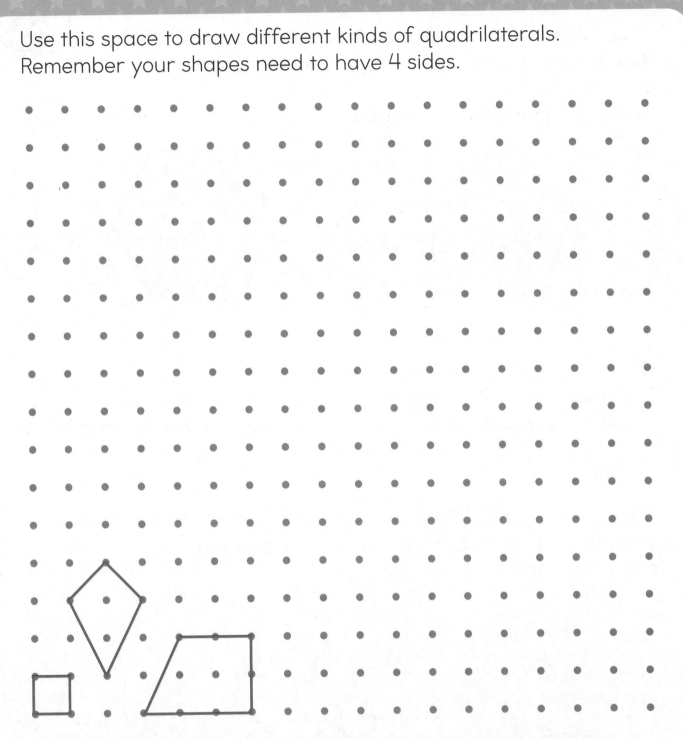

Can you name the shapes you have drawn? Look back at the previous page to help you remember the names of the shapes.

Note for parent: Refer to the descriptions on the previous page to help your child to identify the names of the different quadrilaterals.

233

Pentagons and Hexagons

A **pentagon** has 5 sides and a **hexagon** has 6 sides.
Regular pentagons and hexagons have equal angles and equal sides.
Write the names of the shapes.

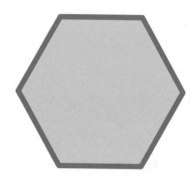

....

....

The United States Pentagon building is shaped like a

....

It has 5 sides and 5 floors, and the central pentagonal plaza is 5 acres in area.

The cells in the bees' honeycomb are shaped like a

....

Draw more hexagons on the honeycomb.

Note for parent: Look for examples of regular shapes around the home, for example, in floor and wall tiling, wallpaper, and fabric patterns.

Irregular Pentagons and Hexagons

Here are some **irregular** pentagons and hexagons. They are irregular because not all their angles and sides are equal. Count the sides to label each one correctly.

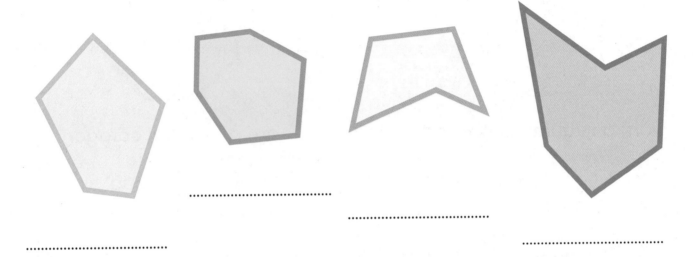

....

....

Draw more pentagons and hexagons below. Use the dots to help you draw straight lines. Label your shapes.

pentagon
....

....

....

Note for parent: Any shape with 5 straight sides is a pentagon and any shape with 6 straight sides is a hexagon.

Heptagons and Octagons

Study the shapes below. Complete the descriptions.

I am a **regular heptagon**.

I have ⬚ equal sides.

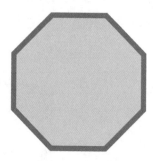

I am a **regular octagon**.

I have ⬚ equal sides.

Irregular heptagons and octagons have unequal sides.

Sort the shapes by coloring them in, using the key below.

octagons = orange

heptagons = blue

hexagons = red

pentagons = green

Note for parent: Have fun extending this activity by drawing more irregular heptagons and octagons of your own.

Shapes Puzzle

Label the shapes then find the names of the shapes in the wordsearch. Look across, down, diagonally, and backward!

sq....................

o........................

tr........................

h........................

p........................

tr........................

k........................

p........................

rh........................

r........................

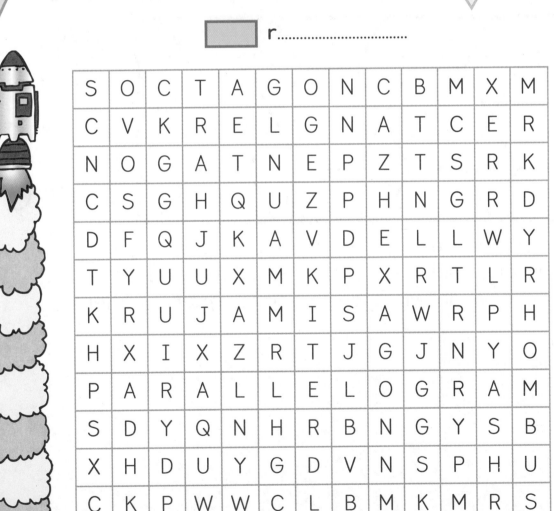

S	O	C	T	A	G	O	N	C	B	M	X	M
C	V	K	R	E	L	G	N	A	T	C	E	R
N	O	G	A	T	N	E	P	Z	T	S	R	K
C	S	G	H	Q	U	Z	P	H	N	G	R	D
D	F	Q	J	K	A	V	D	E	L	L	W	Y
T	Y	U	U	X	M	K	P	X	R	T	L	R
K	R	U	J	A	M	I	S	A	W	R	P	H
H	X	I	X	Z	R	T	J	G	J	N	Y	O
P	A	R	A	L	L	E	L	O	G	R	A	M
S	D	Y	Q	N	H	R	B	N	G	Y	S	B
X	H	D	U	Y	G	D	V	N	S	P	H	U
C	K	P	W	W	C	L	B	M	K	M	R	S
P	L	R	T	R	A	P	E	Z	O	I	D	J

Shapes Pattern

Use the color key to color the shapes in the tile pattern.

hexagons = yellow

rhombuses = orange

trapezoids = purple

triangles = blue

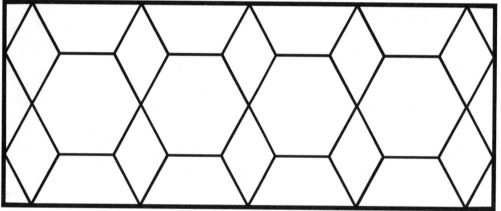

Create your own tile pattern in the space below.
Use only straight-sided shapes. Name all the different
shapes you have drawn. Then color it to create a pattern.

Note for parent: Straight-sided shapes fit together without any gaps (we call this tessellation).
Look for shapes and patterns in and around the home, and your local environment.

Circles and Ovals

Circles are round shapes that have no angles and no straight sides.

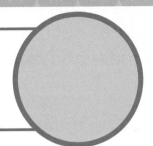

Look around your home for circles. Write the names of some things that are circular.

....

....

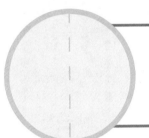 We can cut a circle into two equal parts to make **semicircles**.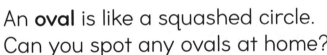

An **oval** is like a squashed circle. Can you spot any ovals at home?

Label these objects: **circle**, **semicircle**, or **oval**.

1. .... 2. .... 3. .... 4. ....

Note for parent: You could play a version of the game I Spy using shapes, for example, "I spy with my little eye something that is a circle shape."

239

Solid Shapes

Flat shapes such as triangles, quadrilaterals, pentagons, and hexagons are **2-dimensional**. Solid shapes are **3-dimensional**.

Draw a line to match each label to the correct solid shape.

4.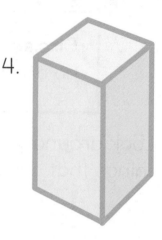

1.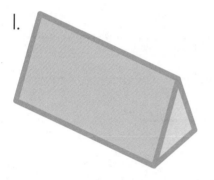

sphere

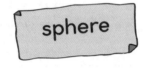
pyramid

5.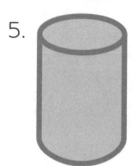

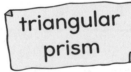
triangular prism

2.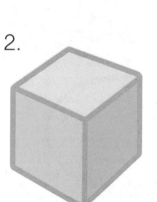

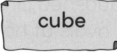
cube

6.

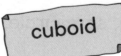
cuboid

3.

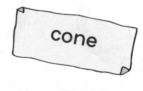
cone

7.

cylinder

Molly took a solid shape and drew around all its faces.

What is Molly's shape called? ....

Mo took a different shape and drew around its faces.

What is Mo's shape called? ....

Milly drew around this shape.

What is Milly's shape called? ....

The faces on Joe's shape looked like this.

What is Joe's shape called? ....

Shape Building

Fabio has made these shapes from cubes.
How many cubes has he used?

cubes

cubes

Emily has put 2 triangles together in different ways to make new shapes. Name the new shapes she has made.

1. ....

2. ....

3. ....

4. ....

Area with Square Units

The space that a shape covers is called the **area** of the shape. We can measure area using squares.

This is **one square unit.**

Count the squares to find the area of the shaded shapes.

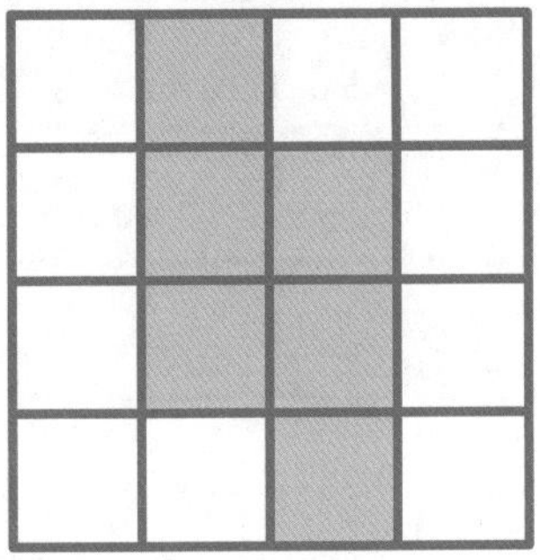

square units

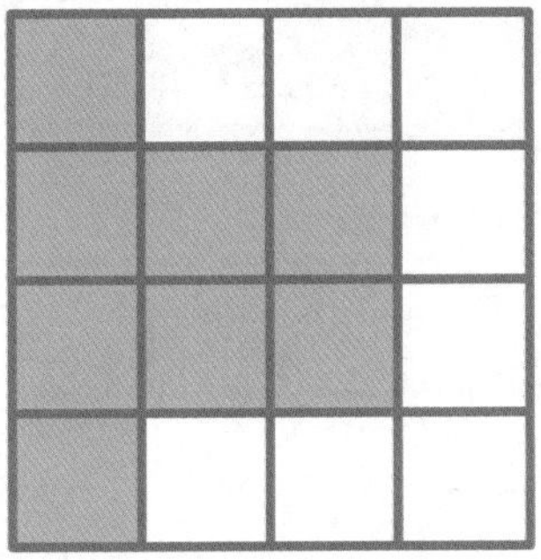

square units

square units

square units

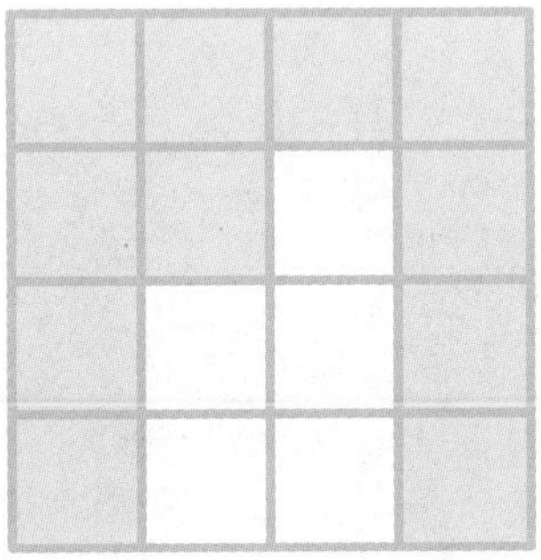

square units

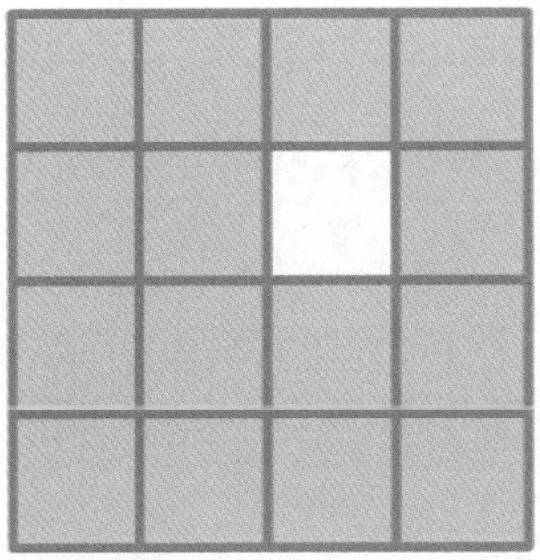

square units

Note for parent: This activity introduces your child to the language we use when talking about area.

243

Area with Half Units

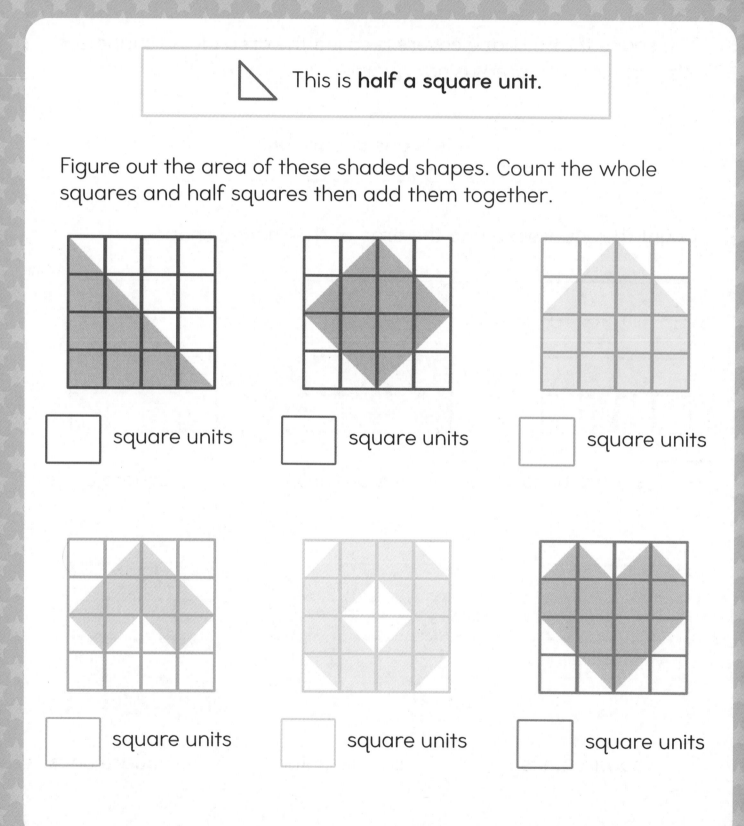

This is **half a square unit.**

Figure out the area of these shaded shapes. Count the whole squares and half squares then add them together.

☐ square units

☐ square units

☐ square units

☐ square units

☐ square units

☐ square units

Note for parent: Your child should know that two half squares make one whole square.

Length and Width

The longest side of a shape is called the **length**.
The shortest side is the **width**.
Count the squares to find the length and width of this shape.

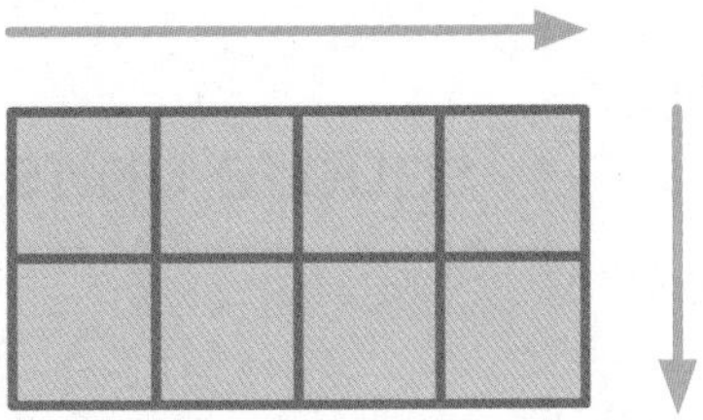

length ☐ squares

width ☐ squares

We don't need to count all the squares!

The length multiplied by the width is the area of the shape.

4 x 2 = 8   length x width = area

Find the area of these shapes by multiplying length x width.

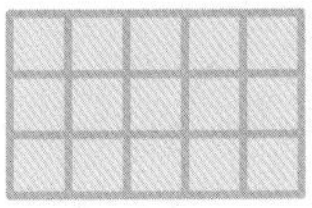

length ☐ width ☐ area ☐ square units

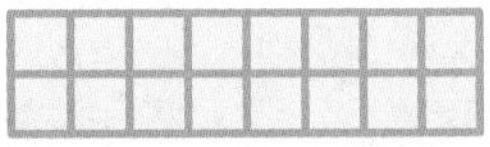

length ☐ width ☐ area ☐ square units

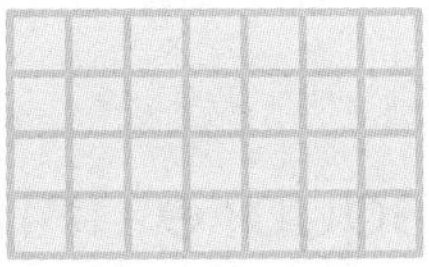

length ☐ width ☐ area ☐ square units

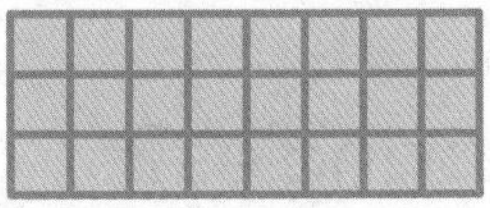

length ☐ width ☐ area ☐ square units

Note for parent: Children should know that when we multiply length by width, we get the same answer as when counting squares. It's a shortcut to finding the area!

Area of Flat Shapes

Multiply the length by the width to find the area of these flat shapes.

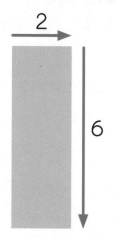
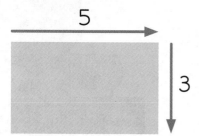
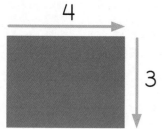

3

3

☐ x ☐ = ☐ square units

5

3

☐ x ☐ = ☐ square units

2

6

☐ x ☐ = ☐ square units

4

3

☐ x ☐ = ☐ square units

What do you notice about the area of the last two rectangles?

Note for parent: Study the last two rectangles—they have the same area but are different shapes.

Area of Irregular Shapes

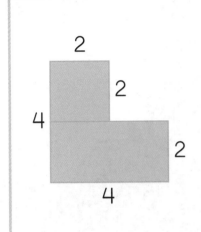

To work out the area of this shape, treat it as two shapes.
One is a square of area 2 x 2 and the other is a rectangle of area 4 x 2. Add the areas together.

2 x 2 = 4
4 x 2 = 8
Total area = 12 square units

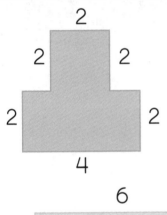

Total area = ☐ square units

Total area = ☐ square units

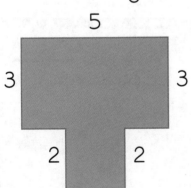

Total area = ☐ square units

Area Problems

A vegetable garden is 5 feet long and 4 feet wide.

What is the total area of the garden?

☐ square feet

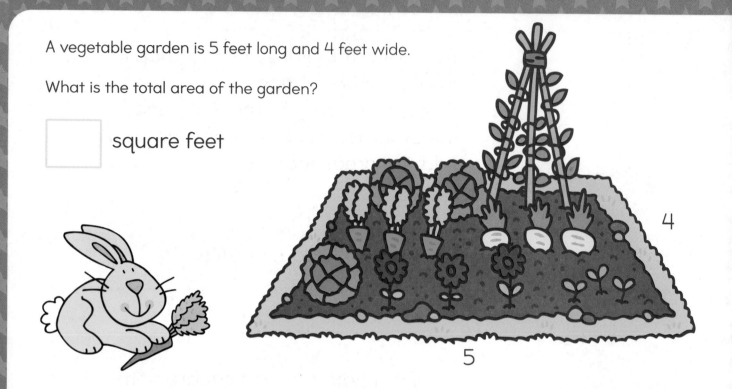

A backyard pool is 20 feet in length by 10 feet wide.

What is the total area of the pool?

☐ square feet

Jenny wants to buy carpet

for two bedrooms in her house.

One bedroom is 14 feet long

and 10 feet wide. The other

bedroom is 12 feet long and

10 feet wide.

What is the total area of carpet

that she needs to buy?

Use the diagrams to help you

figure out the problem.

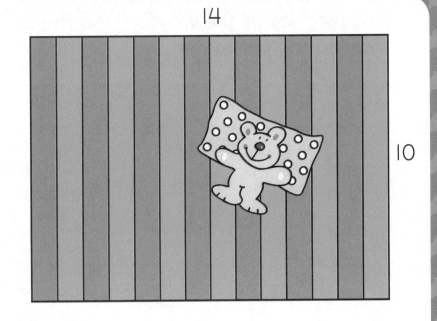

14

10

Total area = ☐ square feet

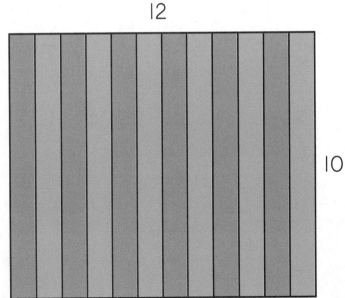

12

10

Perimeter

The distance all the way around the sides of a flat shape is called the **perimeter**.

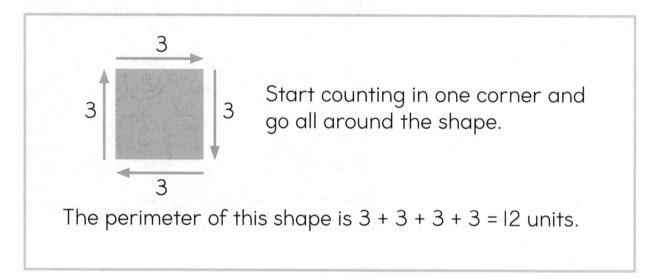

Start counting in one corner and go all around the shape.

The perimeter of this shape is 3 + 3 + 3 + 3 = 12 units.

Find the perimeter of these shapes by adding the lengths of all the sides.

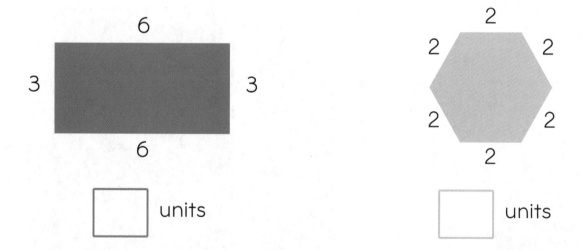

☐ units

☐ units

Note for parent: Knowing the properties of shapes will help your child make quicker calculations. For example, a square has equal sides so we can multiply the length of one side by 4.

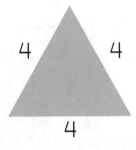

4

4   4

4

☐ units

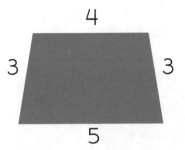

4

3   3

5

☐ units

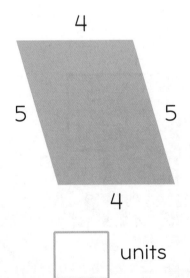

4

5   5

4

☐ units

3   3

5   5

☐ units

Perimeter Puzzles

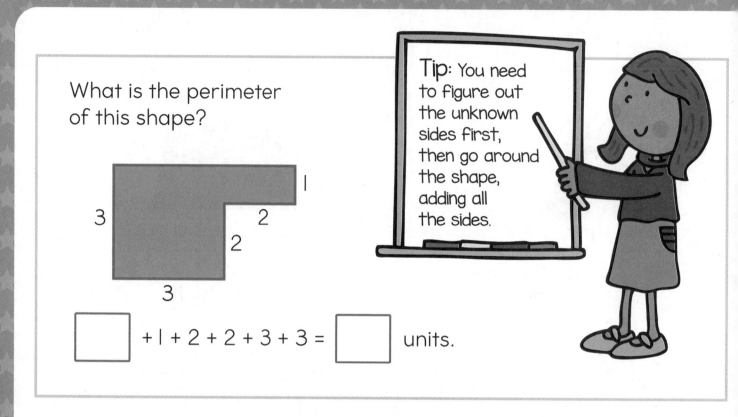

What is the perimeter of this shape?

Tip: You need to figure out the unknown sides first, then go around the shape, adding all the sides.

3

1

2

2

3

☐ + 1 + 2 + 2 + 3 + 3 = ☐ units.

Find the perimeter of these shapes.

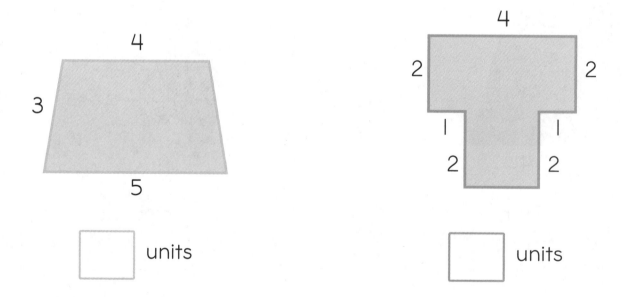

4

3

5

☐ units

4

2

2

1

1

2

2

☐ units

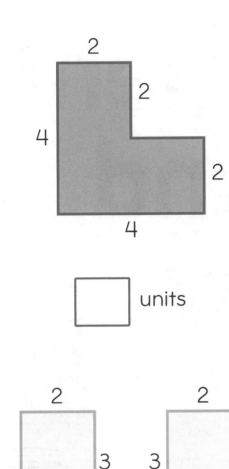

2

2

4

2

4

☐ units

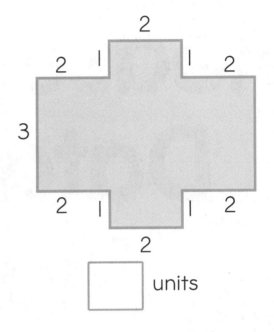

2

2 1 1 2

3

2 1 1 2

2

☐ units

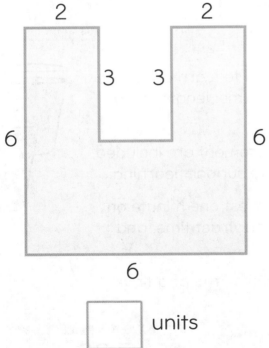

2

2

3 3

6

6

6

☐ units

Measurement, Data, and Money

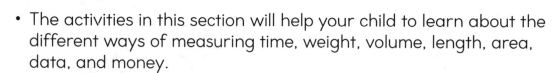

Helping Your Child

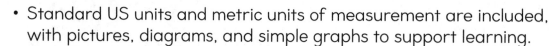

- The activities in this section will help your child to learn about the different ways of measuring time, weight, volume, length, area, data, and money.

- Standard US units and metric units of measurement are included, with pictures, diagrams, and simple graphs to support learning.

- Your child will learn to tell the time to the nearest one minute on analog and digital clocks. They will add and subtract time, and solve problems.

- Set aside time to do the activities together. Do a little at a time, so that your child enjoys learning.

- The answers begin on page 318.

7:30 am

Contents

Time to the Nearest 5 Minutes

Write the time shown on the clocks in two different ways.
For example:

3:05
....
5 minutes past 3
....

6:50
....
10 minutes to 7
....

Now try these:

....

....

....

....

....

....

Time Passes

Compare the time on the left with the time on the right.
How much time has passed?

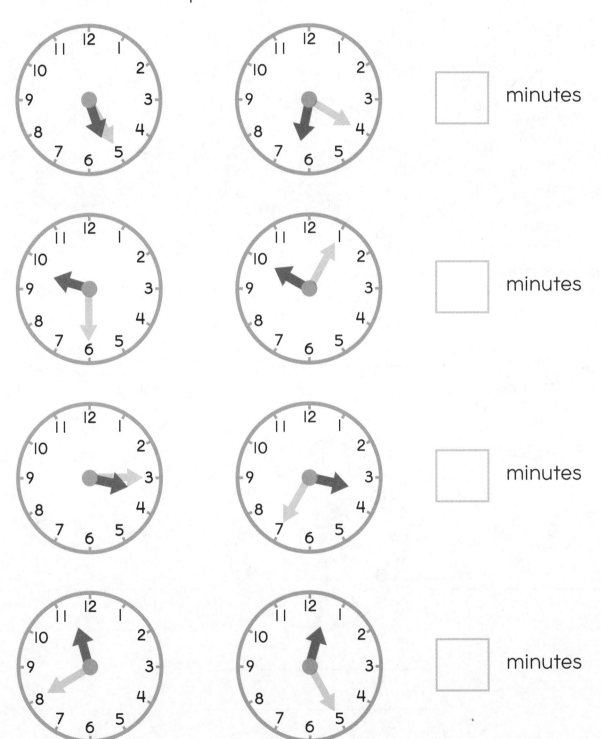

minutes

minutes

minutes

minutes

Time to the Nearest Minute

Write the time shown on the clocks in two different ways.

4:03

3 minutes past 4

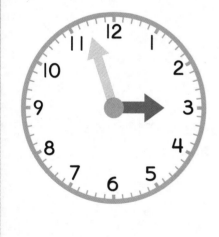

Note for parent: Your child will need to look very closely at the minute hand to distinguish each minute on the clock.

Morning and Evening Times

The time between 12 midnight and 12 noon is called **a.m.**

The time between 12 noon and 12 midnight is called **p.m.**

Read the puzzles. Write the time and write a.m. or p.m.

1. Early one morning, Mina went for a walk with her dog. She set off at 8:12 and arrived back home half an hour later. What time did she arrive home?

   8 : 42 a.m.

2. School lunch starts at 12:00 noon and ends one and a quarter hours later. What time does lunch end?

   ....

3. Jay had baseball practice for 40 minutes in the evening. If baseball practice ended at 7:30, what time did it start?

   ....

4. Becky played on her computer after school for 30 minutes then she started her homework at 5:45. What time did she begin playing on the computer?

   ....

Note for parent: This activity introduces the concept of a.m. and p.m. times, and the addition and subtraction of time.

259

Digital Clocks

Digital clocks don't have hands, they show the time in numbers only. The digits before the colon (the dots) show the hour and the last two digits show the minutes.

Write the time for each digital clock.

Try these:

18 minutes past 6

7 minutes to 8

....

....

....

....

....

....

Subtracting Time

Read the time on the digital clocks and figure out the correct times.
You can use the timeline to help you.

0   3 a.m.   6 a.m.   9 a.m.   12 p.m.   3 p.m.   6 p.m.   9 p.m.   12 a.m.

6:00 pm

What time was it 3 hours ago?

Write the time. ....

3:00 pm

What time was it 5 hours ago?

Write the time. ....

12:00 pm

What time was it 7 hours ago?

Write the time. ....

9:00 am

What time was it 4 and a half hours ago?

Write the time. ....

Note for parent: This activity gives further practice in distinguishing between a.m. and p.m. times, and the subtraction of time.

261

Time Problems

Answer these time problems.

Remember, there are 60 seconds in a minute, 60 minutes in an hour, and 24 hours in a day.

1. If Amy chatted on the phone to a friend for 1 hour and 5 minutes, how many minutes was that?

☐ minutes

2. If the movie started at 4 and finished at 5:30, how long was the movie in minutes?

☐ minutes

3. How many hours are there between 9 a.m. on Saturday and 9 a.m. on Sunday?

☐ hours

4. If Amir won the race by 1 and a quarter minutes, how many seconds was that?

☐ seconds

Note for parent: This activity practices conversions of days to hours, hours to minutes, and minutes to seconds.

More Time Problems

Use the timeline or the clocks below to help you solve these time problems. Write a.m. or p.m. after the time.

0   3 a.m.   6 a.m.   9 a.m.   12 p.m.   3 p.m.   6 p.m.   9 p.m.   12 a.m.

1. I was 15 minutes late for my early morning swimming lesson. If I arrived at 7:30, what time did my lesson start?

....

2. If school starts at 9:05 in the morning and ends 6 hours later. What time does school end?

....

3. If a flight set off at 6:20 in the evening and arrived 4 hours and 10 minutes later, what time did the flight land?

....

4. In wintertime, if sunrise was at 7:00 and sunset was 9 and a half hours later, what time was sunset?

....

5 Minutes Later

Read the time on each clock. Write what the time will be five minutes later, on the clock on the right. The first one is done for you.

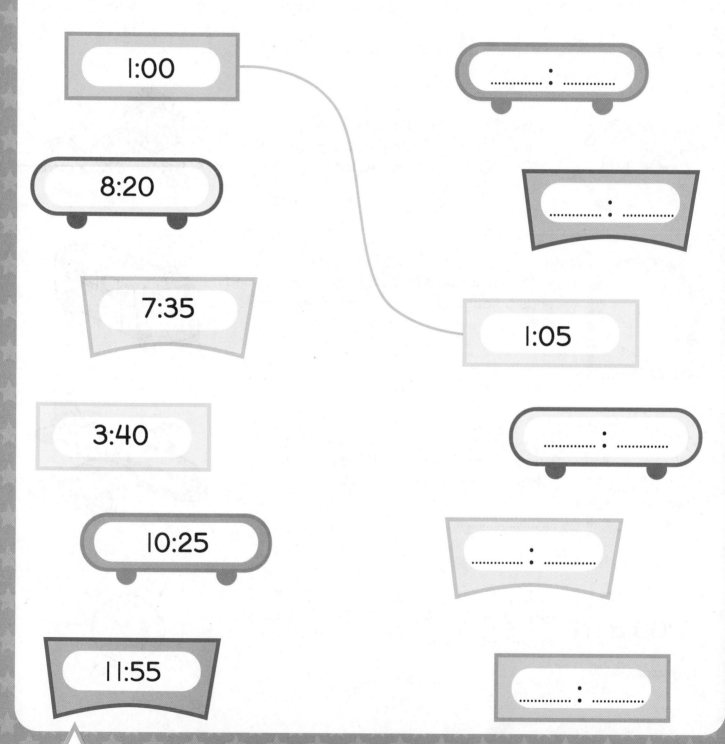

1:00

8:20

7:35

3:40

10:25

11:55

.... : ....

.... : ....

1:05

.... : ....

.... : ....

.... : ....

Note for parent: Look at your watch, or a clock in your home, and ask your child what time it will be after 5 minutes has passed.

Draw the Times

Draw the hands on the clocks below to show these times. The first one has been done for you.

1:00	4:15	11:05

5:30	7:25	6:55

Note for parent: Encourage your child to draw the clocks as accurately as they can.

265

Write the Times

Read the times then write the times in numbers on the digital clocks. The first one is done for you.

1. half-past 8

2. 5 minutes past 2

3. quarter past 7

4. 20 minutes past 10

5. 5 minutes past 9

6. quarter past 3

7. half-past 12

8. 35 minutes past 5

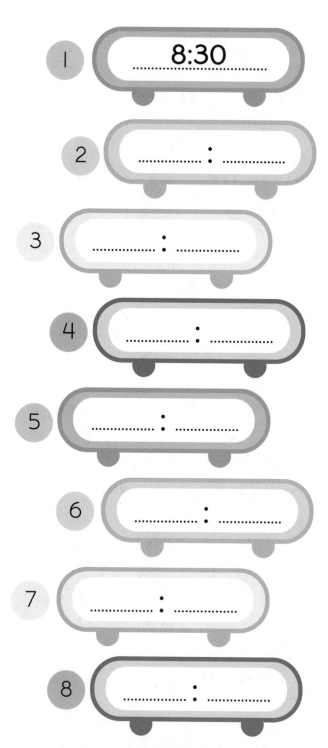

1 8:30

2 .... : ....

3 .... : ....

4 .... : ....

5 .... : ....

6 .... : ....

7 .... : ....

8 .... : ....

Note for parent: Extend this activity by making up some more clock times for your child to write.

Reading a Calendar

Read the calendar to help you answer the questions below.

July

MONDAY	TUESDAY	WEDNESDAY	THURSDAY	FRIDAY	SATURDAY	SUNDAY
						1
2	3	4	5	6	7	8
9	10	11	12	13	14	15
16	17	18	19	20	21	22
23	24	25	26	27	28	29
30	31					

1. How many days are there in July? ....

2. Independence Day is on the 4th of July, what day of the week is this?

....

3. What date is one week after the 12th of July? ....

4. What date is the third Sunday in July? ....

5. If today's date is the 21st of July, what date is the day after tomorrow?

....

6. What day of the week will the 1st of August be on?

....

Note for parent: Learn the rhyme "30 days have September, April, June, and November. All the rest have 31, except February alone, which has 28 days clear, and 29 in a leap year."

Pounds, Ounces, and Tons

What unit of measurement would you choose to measure the weight of the things below?

| 16 ounces = 1 pound | 2,000 pounds = 1 ton |

pounds / ounces

pounds / tons

ounces / tons

pounds / tons

pounds / ounces

tons / ounces

Note for parent: Discuss the reasons why we need to know the weight of items. For example, why are passengers' suitcases weighed before putting them on an airplane?

Grams and Kilograms

The metric system uses grams and kilograms for measuring weight.

> **1,000 grams = 1 kilogram**

Read the scales and mark Toni's homework. Put a check ✔ for a correct answer and an ✗ for a wrong answer. Correct any mistakes.

☐ The grapes weigh the most.

☐ The cherries weigh 30 grams less than the banana.

☐ The banana weighs 10 grams more than the grapes.

☐ Two bananas would weigh 180 grams.

☐ The cherries plus the grapes would weigh 130 grams.

☐ The grapes and a banana would weigh 150 grams.

☐ 10 bananas would weigh less than one kilogram.

☐ $\frac{1}{2}$ kilogram = 400 grams

60g

70g

90g

Note for parent: This activity will help to introduce your child to the metric units that are used to measure weight.

269

Missing Weights

Figure out the missing weights to balance the scales.
Then write the missing weights on the packages.

Remember:
16 oz = 1 lb

Write **lb** for pounds. Write **oz** for ounces.

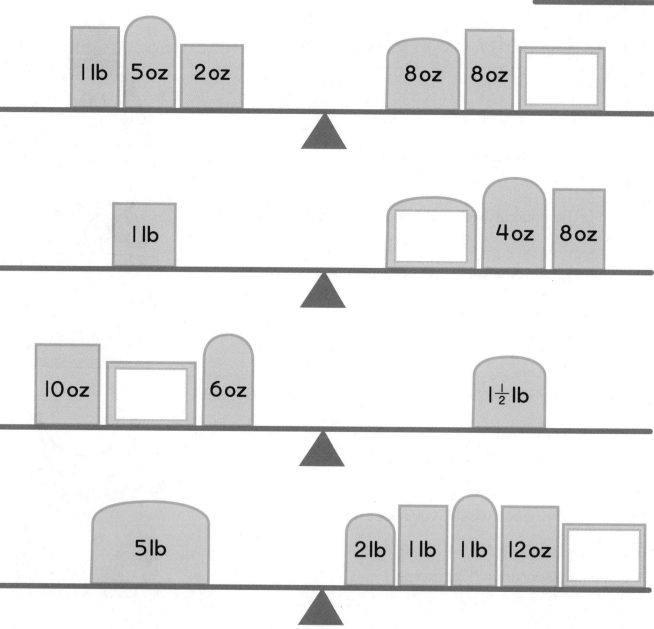

Note for parent: This activity practices basic algebra in a visual way.

Estimate the Weight

Look at each of the objects below and estimate the weight. Circle the best answer.

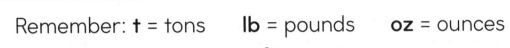

Remember: **t** = tons   **lb** = pounds   **oz** = ounces

(**4oz**) or **4lb**

3lb or **3oz**

5oz or **1lb**

10lb or **1t**

20oz or **20lb**

1oz or **1lb 12oz**

Now look at the shopping list and figure out the total weights of the items. Write the totals in the table.

Items	Weight
3 pairs of socks	9 oz
4 apples	
6 cupcakes	

Note for parent: Check the weight of the food items in your cupboard—the weight is printed on the packaging. Try guessing first! Whose guess is closest?

271

Measuring Capacity

When we measure liquids, we can use cups, pints, and quarts.

8 ounces = 1 cup (**c**)   2 cups = 1 pint (**pt**)
2 pints = 4 cups, or 1 quart (**qt**)

How much juice is in each measuring cup?

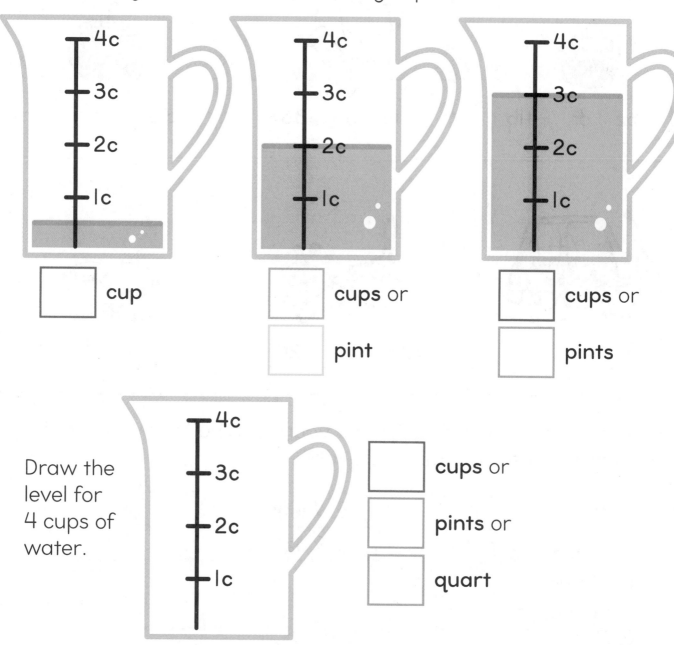

| | cup |

| | **cups** or |
| | pint |

| | **cups** or |
| | pints |

Draw the level for 4 cups of water.

	cups or
	pints or
	quart

Quarts and Gallons

Remember...

16 cups, or 8 pints, or 4 quarts = 1 gallon (**gal**)

What unit of measurement would you use to measure the capacity of the following containers? Circle the best answer.

pints or **gallons**

quarts or **cups**

gallons or **ounces**

pints or **gallons**

cups or **quarts**

pints or **ounces**

quarts or **gallons**

Note for parent: Capacity is the amount of liquid a container can hold. Different units of measurement are used for larger and smaller containers.

273

Milliliters and Liters

The metric system uses milliliters and liters to measure capacity.

1,000 milliliters (**ml**) = 1 liter (**l**)   500 **ml** = $\frac{1}{2}$ **l**   250 **ml** = $\frac{1}{4}$ **l**

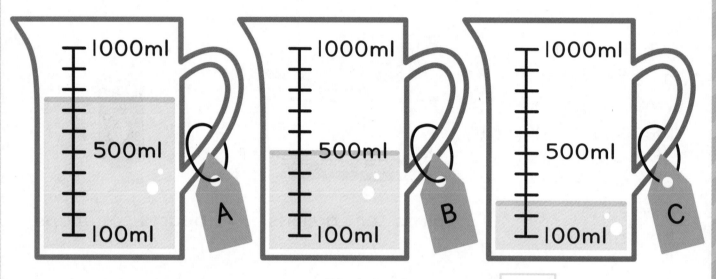

Which measuring cup has half a liter of liquid?   B

Which measuring cup is three-quarters full?   ☐

Which two measuring cups together total one liter of liquid?   ☐ ☐

Would you expect a glass to hold more or less than a liter of water?
Circle: **more / less.**

Would you expect a teapot to hold 1 liter, 10 liters, or 20 liters?

☐

Note for parent: For further practice, show your child how to use measuring cups or containers found in your kitchen to measure different amounts of water.

Problems with Capacity

Figure out the answers to these problems.

1. If one teaspoon of medicine is 5 milliliters, how many teaspoons of medicine are in a 30-milliliter bottle?

[ ] **teaspoons**

2. If one glass of juice is 150 milliliters, how much is two glasses?

[ ] **milliliters**

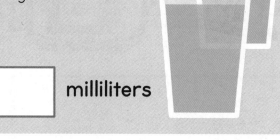

3. If one can of soda is 330 milliliters, how much is three cans?

[ ] **milliliters**

4. From one liter of juice, how many 100-milliliter glasses could I fill?

[ ] **glasses**

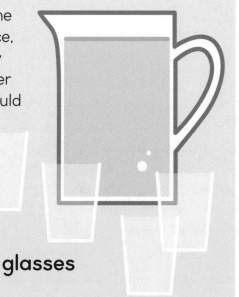

5. From one liter of milk, how many 500-milliliter bottles could I fill?

[ ] **bottles**

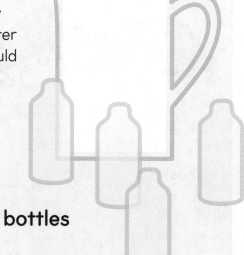

Note for parent: Useful equivalents: one liter is just over two pints, 500 milliliters is one pint, and one cup is around 235 milliliters.

Halves and Fourths of an Inch

Use the ruler to measure the length of each object.
Write the answer below.

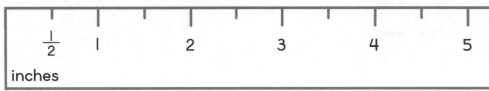

$4\frac{1}{2}$ inches

inches

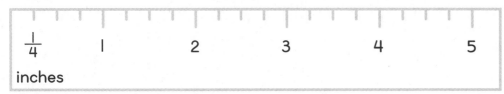

inches

Note for parent: This activity practices measuring in halves and fourths (or quarters) of an inch. Count along the scale: $\frac{1}{4}$, $\frac{1}{2}$, $\frac{3}{4}$, 1, $1\frac{1}{4}$, $1\frac{1}{2}$, etc.

More Halves and Fourths

Use the ruler to draw the following objects.

A tadpole that is $1\frac{1}{4}$ inches long.

A damsel fly that is $2\frac{1}{2}$ inches long.

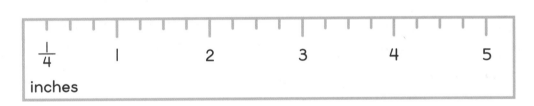

A worm that is $3\frac{3}{4}$ inches long.

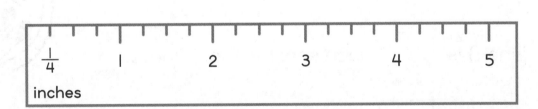

Note for parent: Mark the end point of each drawing first. Then try to draw accurately against the scale.

277

Measuring and Comparing

Measure the colored lines using the ruler below and compare the lengths.

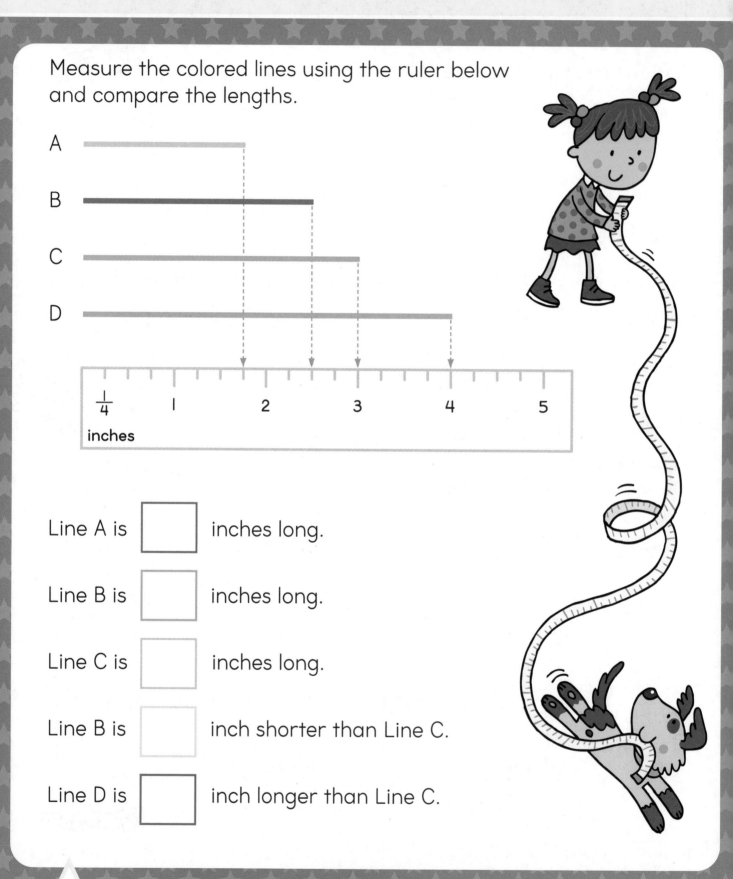

Line A is ☐ inches long.

Line B is ☐ inches long.

Line C is ☐ inches long.

Line B is ☐ inch shorter than Line C.

Line D is ☐ inch longer than Line C.

Note for parent: This activity practices measuring in whole numbers, halves, and quarters.

Feet, Yards, and Miles

Estimate the length of the following things.

| 12 inches (**in**) = 1 foot (**ft**)   3 feet = 1 yard (**yd**)   1,760 yards = 1 mile (**ml**) |

Circle more or less than one **foot**.

more / less   more / less   more / less

Circle more or less than one **yard**.

more / less   more / less   more / less

Circle more or less than one **mile**.

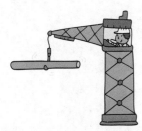

more / less   more / less   more / less

Metric Measures

The metric system uses millimeters and centimeters to measure shorter lengths.
For longer lengths, meters and kilometers are used.

10 millimeters (**mm**) = 1 centimeter (**cm**)
100 centimeters = 1 meter (**m**)
1,000 meters = 1 kilometer (**km**)

Where are the arrows pointing? Write the missing lengths in the boxes below.

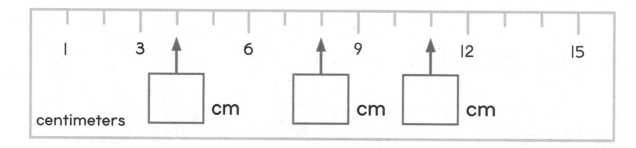

Which unit of metric measurement would you use to measure the following:

Your height? ....

Your foot? ....

Your pencil? ....

Your bedroom? ....

The distance to your nearest town or city?

....

Note for parent: Help your child to fill in the details for as many of the above measurements as you can.

Long and Short Measures

Figure out the answers to these word problems.

1. Charlie is 20 cm tall. Buster is 30 cm taller. How tall is Buster?

☐ **cm tall**

2. Jamie is 125 cm tall. To ride the roller coaster, he needs to be 140 cm tall. How much taller does he need to be?

☐ **cm taller**

3. Ellie's scarf is 88 cm long. How much shorter than 100 cm is it?

☐ **cm shorter**

4. Rosie has a roll of wrapping paper that is 90 cm long. If she cuts it into three equal lengths, how many centimeters long is each length of paper?

☐ **cm long**

Note for parent: Think of some similar problems you can ask your child and work out the answers together.

281

Measuring Irregular Perimeters

To measure this wavy line, place a length of string on top of the line following its shape closely. Cut the string at the end of the line. Pull the string straight and measure it.

This wavy line is [ ] **in** (or **cm**) long.

Measure the perimeter of this pond. Estimate first then measure using a length of string and a ruler.

The perimeter of the pond:

My estimate is [ ] **in** (or **cm**).

The actual measurement is [ ] **in** (or **cm**).

Note for parent: Remind your child of the meaning of the term "perimeter," i.e., the distance around a shape. You can measure in inches or centimeters.

Measuring Irregular Areas

To measure the area of an irregular shape like the pond, we can divide the shape up into square units. Like this:

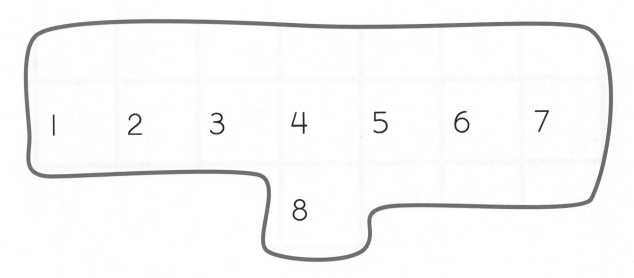

Now count the whole squares and half squares:

number of whole squares = ☐

number of half squares = ☐

Note: If there are 10 half squares, count this as 5 whole squares.

Next, add the numbers together to get the total number of square units.

☐ + ☐ = **square units**

Note for parent: This does not need to be an exact measurement, but it will show children one way in which we can measure an irregular area.

283

Same Perimeter, Different Areas

Some shapes can have the same perimeter but different areas.

> **Perimeter** is the outside of the shape.
> **Area** is the inside of the shape.

Work out the perimeter of the green shape by adding the unit lengths of all the sides.

☐ **units**

Work out the area of the green shape by counting the square units inside.

☐ **units**

1

3   3

1

2

2   2

2

Work out the perimeter of the blue shape by adding the unit lengths of all the sides.

☐ **units**

Work out the area of the blue shape by counting the square units inside.

☐ **units**

Which shape has the biggest area: the green or the blue shape?

....

If we put a fence all the way around the perimeter of each shape to make a field, which shape would make the biggest field, the blue or the green shape? ....

Note for parent: Point out that these shapes have the same perimeter but different areas.

Same Area, Different Perimeters

Some shapes can have the same area but different perimeters.

Work out the perimeter and area of each of these shapes.

3

2   2

3

The perimeter of
the yellow shape is: ☐ **units**

The area of the
yellow shape is: ☐ **units**

The perimeter of
the red shape is:

☐ **units**

The area of the
red shape is:

☐ **units**

1

2

3

3

1

4

Which shape has the biggest perimeter: the yellow or

the red shape? ....

Which shape would need the most fencing? ....

Why? ....

Note for parent: Point out that these shapes have the same area but different perimeters. The red shape would need more fencing because it is longer and narrower.

285

Reading a Picture Graph

A picture graph uses pictures or symbols to record data. The table below shows the food that was sold one lunchtime at Carol's Café.

Food	Number of sales		Total	KEY
burger	◯ ◯ ◯ ◯			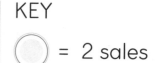 ◯ = 2 sales
pizza	◯ ◯ ◯ ◯ ◖			
pasta	◯ ◯ ◖			
sandwich	◯ ◯ ◯			
salad	◯ ◖			

Study the picture graph to answer these questions.

1. Use the key to figure out the totals. Write the totals in the right-hand column.

2. How many burgers were sold? ....

3. How many more pizzas were sold than pasta?

....

4. Which food was the most popular? ....

5. What was the total number of sales

altogether? ....

Note for parent: This activity provides practice in reading a key and interpreting data from a table.

Drawing a Picture Graph

Use the data in the table below to complete the picture graph for the drinks sold at Carol's Café.

Drinks	Number of sales	Total
tea	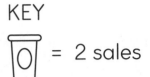	2
coffee		3
soda		9
milkshake		6
orange juice		6

KEY

 = 2 sales

Now answer these questions based on the graph.

1. Which drink sold the most? ....

2. How many fewer coffees were sold than soda?

....

3. Which drinks sold in equal amounts? ....

4. How many milkshakes and orange juices were

sold altogether? ....

5. How many drinks were sold altogether?

....

Note for parent: This activity provides practice in interpreting data from a table and drawing a picture graph.

287

Reading a Bar Graph

A group of students were asked to name their favorite animals at the zoo. The results are shown in the bar graph below.

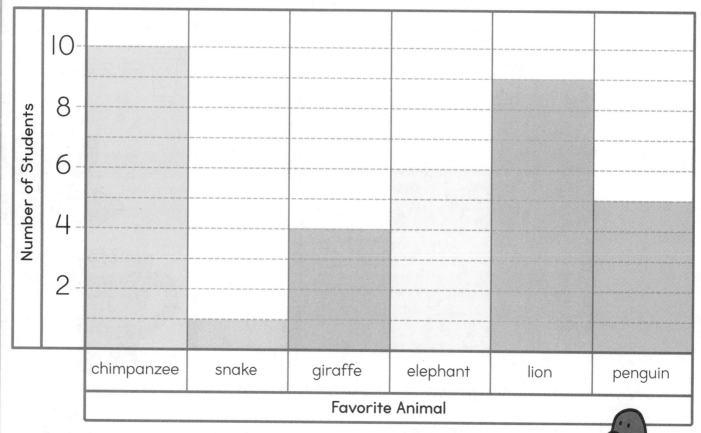

Study the bar graph to answer these questions.

1. How many students said the lion was their favorite animal? ....

2. Which animal was the least popular? ....

3. Which animal was the favorite for most students? ....

4. How many students preferred penguins? ....

5. How many more students preferred elephants to giraffes?

....

Note for parent: This activity provides practice in reading a bar graph and using related math vocabulary.

Drawing a Bar Graph

A group of students were asked to name their favorite pets. The results are shown in the table. Draw a bar graph using the data in the space below.

Favorite Pet	Number of Students
fish	4
dog	11
cat	10
mouse	2
hamster	5
rabbit	9

Number of Students

10

8

6

4

2

fish	dog	cat	mouse	hamster	rabbit

Favorite Pet

Note for parent: Ask your child questions about the Bar graph, for example, "Which is the most popular or least popular pet? How many students prefer cats to rabbits?"

289

Adding Coins—to 50 Cents

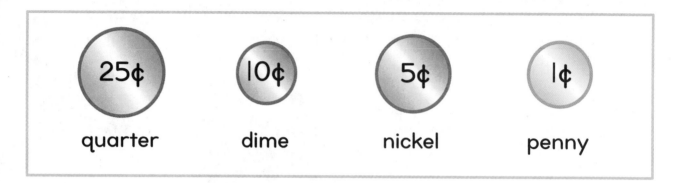

25¢	10¢	5¢	1¢
quarter	dime	nickel	penny

Add up the coins. Write the totals in the boxes.

25¢ + 10¢ + 10¢ = ☐ cents

25　　10　　10

10¢ + 10¢ + 5¢ + 5¢ + 5¢ = ☐ cents

10　　10　　5　　5　　5

10¢ + 5¢ + 5¢ + 5¢ + 1¢ + 1¢ = ☐ cents

10　　5　　5　　5　　1　　1

25¢ + 10¢ + 10¢ + 5¢ = ☐ cents

25　　10　　10　　5

Note for parent: This activity provides practice in adding up coins to 50 cents. You could use real coins if you prefer.

Adding Coins—to One Dollar

Add up the coins. Write the totals in the boxes.

25¢ + 25¢ + 25¢ = ☐ cents

25   25   25

25¢ + 25¢ + 10¢ = ☐ cents

25   25   10

25¢ + 10¢ + 10¢ + 10¢ + 5¢ + 5¢ + 1¢

25   10   10   10   5   5   1

= ☐ cents

25¢ + 25¢ + 25¢ + 10¢ + 10¢ + 5¢

25   25   25   10   10   5

= ☐ cents

Making One Dollar

Add up the coins. Write the total amount in each purse.

A
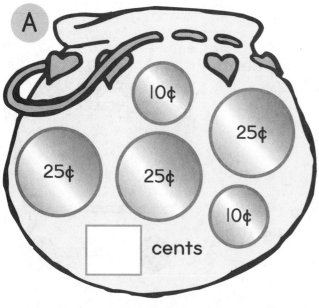

B
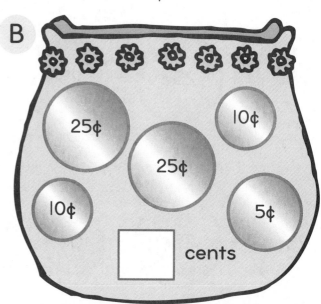

C
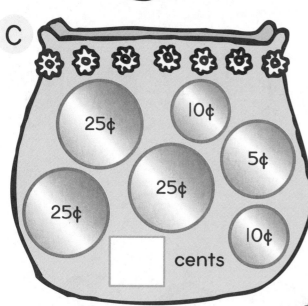

D
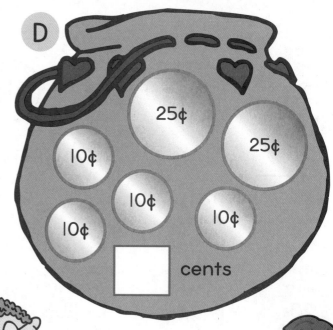

Which purse has exactly one dollar? A, B, C, or D?

....

100 cents = one dollar
100¢ = $1

Note for parent: This activity provides further practice in mental addition of money in amounts up to one dollar. Use real coins if this helps.

Mentar Math—Addition

Read the price list. Work out the total cost for each order.

20¢   60¢   50¢   30¢

+ = ☐ cents

+ = ☐ cents

+ + = ☐ cents

+ + = ☐ cents = ☐ dollar

Coin Puzzles

1. Which two coins make 50 cents?
Write the missing value on the coin.

 25¢   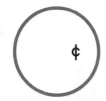 ¢

2. Which two coins make 35 cents?
Write the missing value on the coin.

 25¢   ¢

3. Which three coins make 60 cents?
Write the missing value on the coins.

 25¢   25¢   ¢

4. Which five coins make 25 cents?
Write the missing value on the coins.

 5¢   5¢   5¢   ¢   ¢

5. Which five coins make 40 cents?
Write the missing value on the coins.

 10¢   10¢   10¢   ¢   ¢

Note for parent: Help your child to work out the missing values. You could use real coins to demonstrate the answers.

Money Multiplication

Read the price tags and work out the answers to the questions.

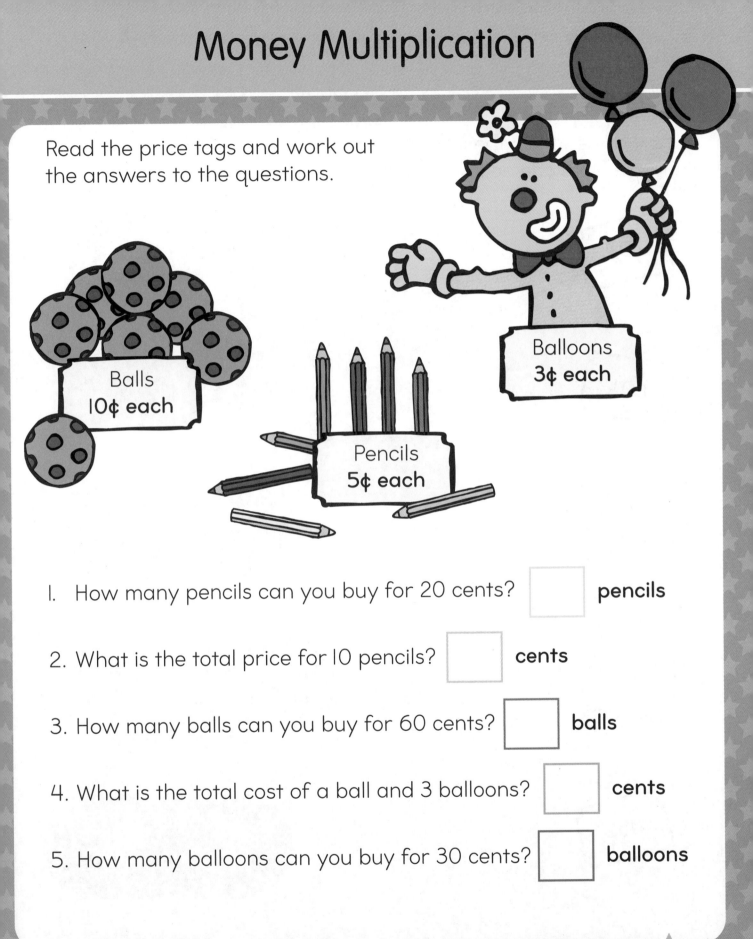

Balls
10¢ each

Pencils
5¢ each

Balloons
3¢ each

1. How many pencils can you buy for 20 cents? ☐ **pencils**

2. What is the total price for 10 pencils? ☐ **cents**

3. How many balls can you buy for 60 cents? ☐ **balls**

4. What is the total cost of a ball and 3 balloons? ☐ **cents**

5. How many balloons can you buy for 30 cents? ☐ **balloons**

Note for parent: Children will need to use their knowledge of multiplication and division to solve these problems.

Money Subtraction

Draw a line to join the price tag to your change from one dollar.

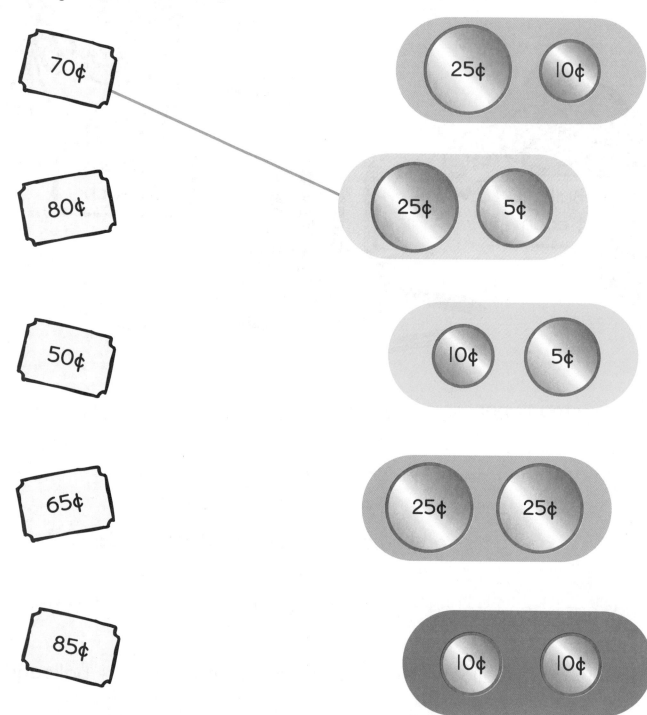

Word Problems with Money

Work out the answers to these word problems. Use a separate piece of paper for your work.

1. It costs 80¢ for a child's ticket on the Rocky Coast Ride. What does it cost for two children?

[ ] **cents**

2. An adult ticket on the bumper cars is one dollar and children ride half price. How much is it for one adult and two children?

[ ] **dollars**

$1

3. Space Racer is 70¢ for an adult and 50¢ for a child. What is the total cost for one adult and one child?

[ ] **cents**

50¢

70¢

4. A ticket for the Go-Karts is $1.20. How much for three tickets?

[ ] **dollars**

and

[ ] **cents**

$1.20

5. The Haunted House is 25¢ for one child. What is the total for four children?

[ ] **cents**

25¢

Note for parent: Remind your child that there are 100 cents in one dollar.

297

Two-step Word Problems

Read the questions and work out the change each time.
Use a separate piece of paper for your work.

1. Molly buys an ice cream for 55¢. She pays with 6 dimes. Figure out how much change she gets.

55¢

[ ] cents

2. Nazim buys 3 used books for 30¢ each and he pays with a dollar bill. How much change does he get?

30¢

[ ] cents

3. Naomi buys a toy robot for $1.50. How much change does she get from 2 dollars?

$1.50

[ ] cents

4. Rory has saved 300¢ in coins. He buys a teddy for $2. How much money does he have left?

$2

[ ] cents

5. Zara has saved 4 quarters and 3 dimes. Is this enough to buy a toy snake costing $1.20? How much will she have left?

$1.20

[ ] cents

Note for parent: Use real coins if you find this helps to solve the problems.

Dollars and Cents

Add the money and write the amount in dollars and cents.

We write one dollar and one penny like this: **$1.01**

We write the dollar before the dot, and the cents (tens and ones) after the dot.

25¢ + 25¢ + 25¢ + 25¢ + 5¢ = $.

$1 + 25¢ + 5¢ = $.

$1 + 10¢ + 10¢ = $.

$2 + $1 + 5¢

= $.

Note for parent: This activity reinforces what your child has already learned about place value with hundreds, tens, and ones.

299

More Dollars and Cents

Add the money and write the amount in dollars and cents.

$1 + 25¢ + 10¢ + 5¢ = $.

$2 + 10¢ + 10¢ + 1¢ = $.

$2 + $1 + 25¢ = $.

$2 + $2 + 1¢ = $.

Note for parent: Look at price labels when out shopping together and practice simple mental addition.

More Word Problems

Work out the answers to these word problems.
Use a separate piece of paper for your work.

1. Emily spends 6 dimes.
She spends twice as much
as Jamie. How much does
Jamie spend?

10¢

☐ **cents**

2. Harry has one dollar.
He buys an apple and gets
75¢ in change. How much
did the apple cost?

$1

☐ **cents**

3. Mom buys 3 bars of candy
at 50¢ each. What is her
change from $2?

50¢

☐ **cents**

4. Dad shares
$2.20 between two
children. How much
do they each get?

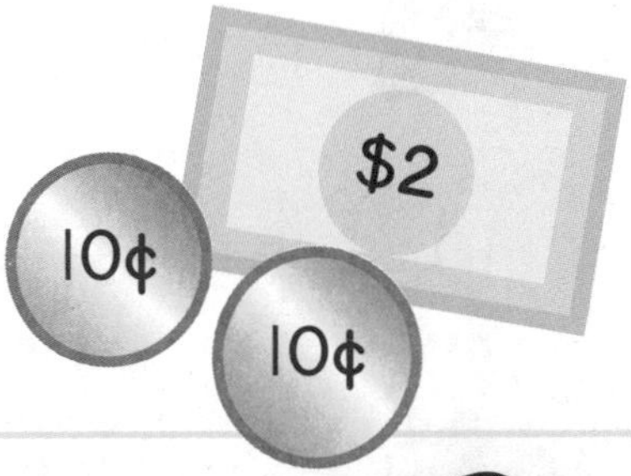

$2

10¢   10¢

☐ **dollar**
and
☐ **cents**

5. Kori has 4 quarters and
5 dimes. How much does he
have left over if he buys
a toy for $1.30?

$1.30

☐ **cents**

Note for parent: This activity practices the four math operations: addition, subtraction, multiplication, and division.

Picture Equations

The pictures in these equations are hidden numbers. You need to figure out what these numbers are, then write the missing numbers in the boxes.

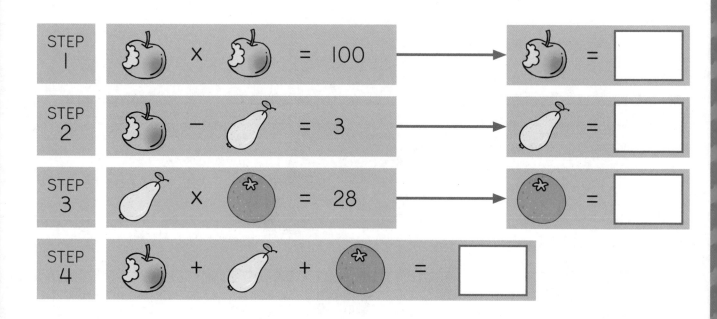

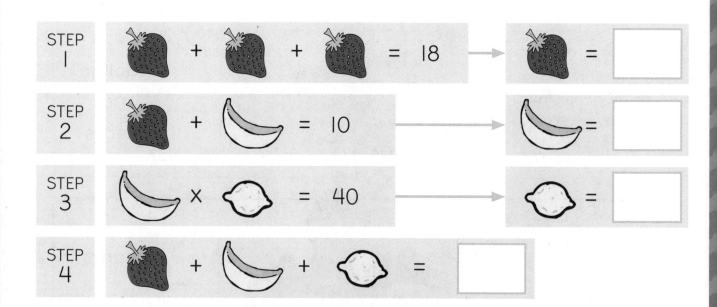

Note for parent: This activity practices logic skills and basic math with numbers up to 100.

More Picture Equations

Here are some more picture equations for you to solve.
Write the missing numbers in the boxes.

| STEP 1 | 🐝 + 🐝 + 🐝 + 🐝 = 20 | 🐝 = ☐ |

| STEP 2 | 🦋 + 🐝 = 25 | 🦋 = ☐ |

| STEP 3 | 🦋 ÷ 🐞 = 5 | 🐞 = ☐ |

| STEP 4 | 🐝 + 🦋 + 🐞 = ☐ |

| STEP 1 | 🎩 + 🎩 + 🎩 = 90 | 🎩 = ☐ |

| STEP 2 | 🧤 + 🎩 = 45 | 🧤 = ☐ |

| STEP 3 | 🧤 ÷ 🧦 = 3 | 🧦 = ☐ |

| STEP 4 | 🎩 + 🧤 + 🧦 = ☐ |

Note for parent: This activity provides further practice in logic and basic math skills.

Skip Counting Review

Skip count down the page and write the missing numbers in the spaces

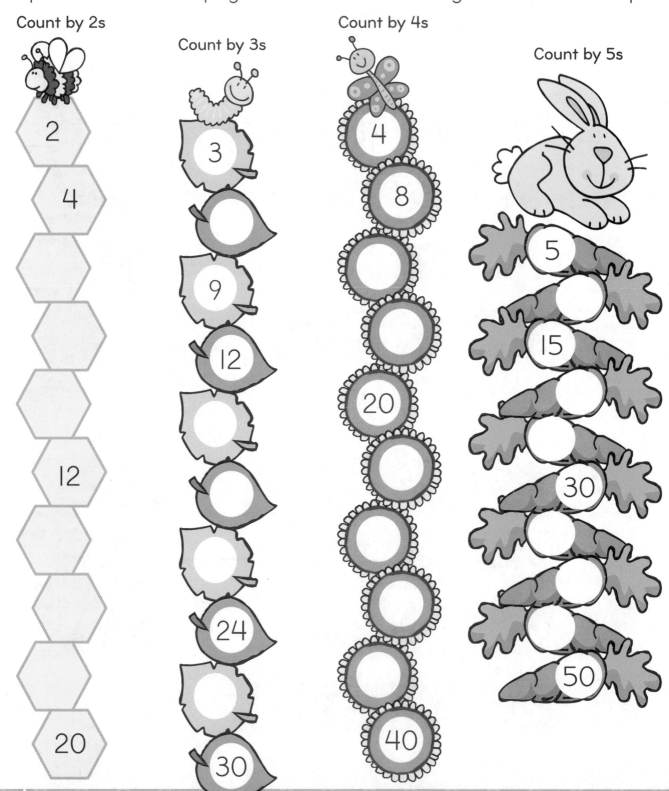

Count by 2s

2
4

12

20

Count by 3s

3

9

12

24

30

Count by 4s

4
8

20

40

Count by 5s

5

15

30

50

Note for parent: This activity provides a valuable review of multiplication facts.

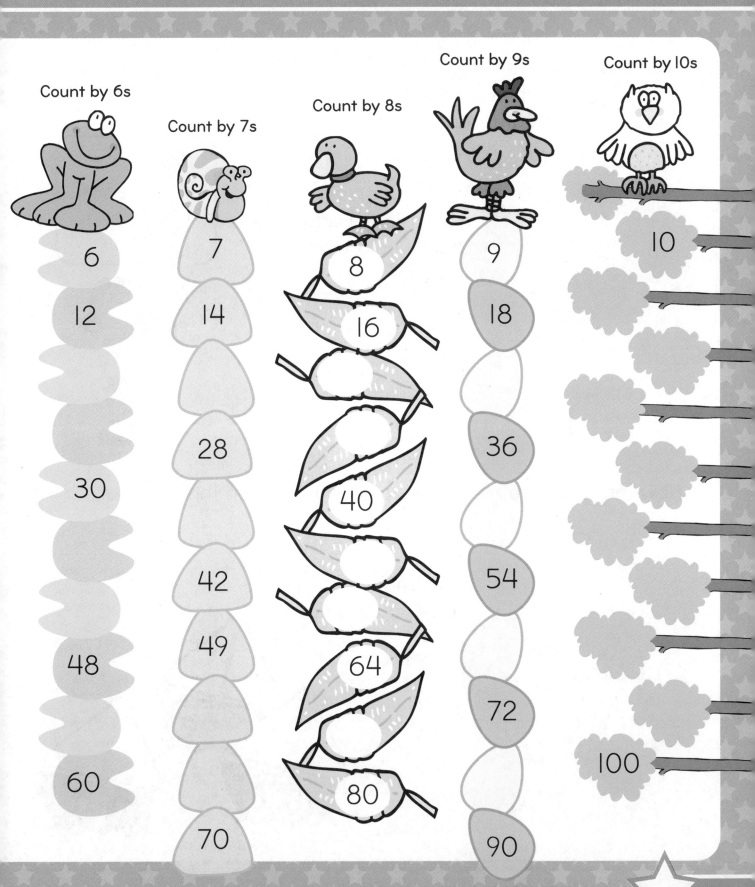

Count by 6s

Count by 7s

Count by 8s

Count by 9s

Count by 10s

6

12

30

48

60

7

14

28

42

49

70

8

16

40

64

80

9

18

36

54

72

90

10

100

Shapes Fun

How many different rectangles can you draw on this pegboard? The pegs form the corners of your shapes. You can overlap the shapes and use different colors.

How many rectangles have you drawn?

Remember squares are rectangles, too.

How many different triangles can you draw on this pegboard?

How many triangles have you drawn?

Note for parent: Draw larger pegboards with more pegs on to squared paper, and try drawing other shapes, including pentagons and hexagons.

Answers

Spelling and Vocabulary

Page 6
Letters a, e, i, o, and u should be colored. Consonants: d, f, j, l, m, n, q, r, v, w, x, y, z.
Possible answers include: h<u>u</u>t, p<u>ea</u>, <u>a</u>pe, t<u>a</u>g, b<u>i</u>ke, ch<u>o</u>p, c<u>a</u>sh, b<u>ea</u>t, b<u>a</u>th, s<u>oa</u>p, st<u>ea</u>k, p<u>a</u>g<u>e</u>s, b<u>oa</u>st, st<u>i</u>ck, t<u>o</u>p<u>i</u>c, sk<u>e</u>tch, b<u>u</u>ck<u>e</u>t.

Page 7
1. dog. 2. sand, socks. 3. friend.
4. bug, bed. 5. gift. 6. bread.

Page 8
From left to right: rain, blue, shoe, tree, goat, light.
There, who, moon, He, eats, cheese, blue, spoon, He, likes, there, where, stars, shine, bright, They, go, always, night, We, nice, tea, So, take, you, me.

Page 9
From left to right: perfect, ninth, object, crept, fourth, subject, strict, swept, seventh, erupt.
1. erupt. 2. seventh. 3. fourth.
4. perfect.

Page 10
um/brel/la, croc/o/dile, tor/na/do, din/o/saur.

Page 11
1. black. 2. blanket. 3. block.
4. cowboy. 5. picture. 6. pirate.
7. snail. 8. snake.

Page 12
annoy, enjoy, toy.
fish, dish, wish.
scribble, nibble, dribble.

Page 13
1. early, because. 2. people, through. 3. biscuit. 4. heard, who.

Page 14
rose: those, nose, goes, throws.
feet: beat, sweet, cheat, street, neat.
pear: square, bear, stare, chair.

Page 15
cold, blue, cough, bed, fright, catch.

Page 16
1. medal. 2. hotel. 3. label. 4. apple.
5. camel. 6. pebble. 7. table.

Page 17
<u>smaller</u>, <u>small</u>est.
<u>bravely</u>, <u>brave</u>st.
bi<u>cycle</u>, tri<u>cycle</u>.
Possible answers include: taller, tallest, farmer, farming, cleverly, cleverest, throwing, thrower, slowly, slowest.

Page 18
unhappy, unable, recall, disappear, reappear, untie.

Page 19
1. impolite. 2. disagree. 3. undo.
4. misbehaving. 5. incorrect.

Page 20
Possible answers include:
The girl bounced on the trampoline.
The boy slipped on the banana.
I washed my hands under the faucet.
The girl was running toward the finish line.

Page 21
subdivide, submerge, submarine, supersonic, supernova, reappear, redo, return.

Page 22
1. bold, 2. foolishly, 3. gracefully.
4. boldly. 5. foolish. 6. graceful.

Page 23
scarily, simply, humbly, spookily, crazily, cuddly, easily, happily.

Page 24
mountain, courage, fame, vigor, joy, envy, venom.

Page 25
pleasure, treasure, measure, picture, nature.

Page 26
solution, fiction, action, position, rotation, invention.
1. action. 2. fiction. 3. invention.
4. position. 5. rotation. 6. solution.

Page 27
1. addition. 2. confusion.
3. correction. 4. decision.
5. subtraction. 6. multiplication.
7. pollution.

Page 28
optician, electrician, magician, politician, musician.

Page 29

Mystery word: scene.

Page 31
From left to right: (veil) height, (eight) receive, (weight) sleigh, (freight) weird, (reindeer) (neighbor)

Answers

1. veil. 2. freight, eight. 3. neighbor, receive. 4. height, weight. 5. reindeer, sleigh. 6. weird.

Page 32
From left to right: (shield) (relief) (field) tried, cried, lie, (brief) (thief) shield, brief, lie, relief, thief, tried.

Page 33
should—could; would—enough; rough—tough; double—trouble.

Page 34
gym, myth, Egypt, cycle, pyramid, mystery.

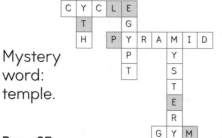

Mystery word: temple.

Page 35
1. information. 2. painter. 3. appointment. 4. departure. 5. punishment. 6. diner. 7. entertainment.

Page 36

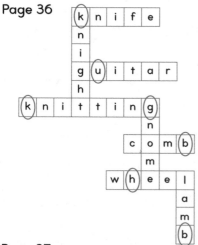

Page 37
Raspberry, ghost, badge, length, climbed, knots, knocked, listened, answer, cupboard, knew, dumb, ghosts.

Page 38
1. our. 2. whether. 3. fair. 4. break. 5. plane. 6. bare.

Page 39
not, knot; here, hear; meddle, medal; tale, tail; ate, eight; knew, new; great, grate.

Page 40
1. change. 2. band. 3. live. 4. tear. 5. band. 6. change. 7. live. 8. bat. 9. tear. 10. bat.

Page 41
blue, stew, through, barbeque, true, crew, new, value, you.

Page 42
Words with soft c sound: rice, dice, city, trace, price, juice, scissors, center, cellar.
Words with hard c sound: crisp, cut, cop, class, cross.

Page 43
1. unicycle. 2. universe. 3. invisible. 4. input. 5. uniform. 6. inflated. 7. inactive.

Page 44
From left to right: bicycle, binoculars, triangle, tripod, biplane, triceratops, tricycle, triplets, trio.

Page 45
Possible answers include: rainbow, bookcase, bookmark, baseball, backpack.
1. crosswalk. 2. suitcase. 3. snowman. 4. notebook. 5. bedroom.

Page 46
1. playground, seesaw.
2. somewhere, sandwich.
3. afternoon, baseball.
4. lifeguard, jellyfish.

Page 47
unfurl, twirl, whirl, hurl, girl.

Page 48
eight, gate, weight, straight, freight, crate, rotate, date, wait, late.

Page 49
1. ti/ger, (tel/e/phone) cook/ie, ham/mer.
2. doc/tor, build/ing, fin/a/ly, (cal/cu/la/tor)
3. el/e/phant, hurr/i/cane, (ed/u/ca/tion) moun/tain.
4. less/on, (hel/i/cop/ter) gar/den, im/por/tant.
pon/tra/di/tious—4 syllables.
scrum/an/elly/wop/ter— 5 syllables.
dock/a/gil/ly—4 syllables.
trill/a/fril/ly—4 syllables.
frap/a/li/cious—4 syllables.

Page 50
eighth, ice, icicles, ice, scenery, ice (or icicles), eighty, scenic, ice, eight (or eighty).

Page 51
1. square, 2. queen, 3. quick, 4. queue, 5. quarter, 6. quack.
Mystery word: squeak.
Possible answers include: quill, quiz, quilt, quake, squid, equal.

Page 52
From left to right: visitor, alligator; sailor, anchor; toaster, dollar, collar; helicopter, actor; sugar, vinegar; polar, color.

Page 53
Words spelled wrong: enuff, deside, brekfast, peeple, anser, becus, nife, possibel, circul.
Correct spelling: enough, decide, breakfast, people, answer, because, knife, possible, circle.

Language Arts

Page 56
1. person—man; place—restaurant; thing—coat.
2. person—Max; place—mall; thing—shoes.

3. person—explorer; place—jungle; thing—map.
4. person—Jemma; place—park; thing—kite.
5. person—astronaut; place—moon; thing—rocket.
6. person—mom; place—kitchen; thing—packed lunch.

Page 57
Mars, Nile, Monday, Great Pyramid, Tuesday, London, China, Wednesday, Tom, The Great Wall of China, Thursday, Japan, Arctic, Friday, New York, Empire State Building, Saturday, Gran, Chalky, Sunday.

Page 58
1. her, 2. she, 3. It, 4. you, me, 5. they, 6. them, 7. mine, 8. their.

Page 59
1. boredom. 2. beauty. 3. love. 4. kindness, bravery. 5. jealousy. 6. trust. 7. curiosity. 8. sorrow, anger. 9. hope. 10. happiness.

Page 60
1. scream. 2. write. 3. run. 4. climb.
1. drive. 2. produces. 3. wave. 4. practices. 5. chooses.

Page 61
1. had. 2. could. 3. is. 4. am. 5. were. 6. was.

Page 62
three, grumpy, four, small, slippery, one, hairy, bitter, moldy, grumpy.
Possible answers include: black bats; small spiders; wriggling worms; slippery snakes.

Page 63
1. Sometimes we have to share with others.
2. The goat trotted nervously across the troll's bridge.
3. Sam was jumping excitedly up and down.
4. Debbie waited quietly in the lunch line.
5. The crowd cheered loudly when the player scored.
Possible answers include:
1. always. 2. softly. 3. Yesterday. 4. kindly.

Page 64
From left to right: glass—glasses; country—countries; quiz—quizzes; scarf—scarves; boat—boats; fox—foxes; puppy—puppies; shelf—shelves; brush—brushes; phone—phones; wife—wives; day—days.

Page 65

N	C	F	R	X	T	E	E	T	H
N	E	A	H	U	P	L	S	K	W
H	J	R	C	D	K	P	H	J	U
M	S	O	D	T	H	O	E	W	Q
D	U	I	F	L	I	E	E	Z	N
V	J	E	F	X	I	P	P	E	L
I	E	C	I	M	P	H	M	M	I
T	F	N	C	J	P	O	C	X	K
E	A	H	R	R	W	A	B	J	V
S	E	O	T	A	T	O	P	B	W

sheep, children, cacti, teeth, feet, mice, potatoes, fish, women, people.

Page 66
The crowd cheered; The crowd cheers; The crowd will cheer.
She danced; She dances; She will dance.
We opened; We open; We will open.
Charlie climbed; Charlie climbs; Charlie will climb.
The dog barked; The dog barks; The dog will bark.
1. We learned how to ride a bike safely.
2. I enjoyed playing basketball with my friends.
1. The teacher will call out our names in class.
2. We will decorate the cake with chocolate icing.

Page 67
1. told, sang. 2. wrote. 3. rang. 4. was. 5. bought. 6. hung. 7. caught. 8. were, begun.

Page 68
sit, wait, walks, sticks, asks, shrug, laughs, skips, hear, stand, waves, says, taps, say, disagree, shakes, lower, believes, asks, clear.

Page 69
We went to the beach. I bought a yummy strawberry ice cream. I had to eat it quickly because it was melting in the sun. Mom and Dad went swimming but I decided to go exploring. I found a rock pool and there was a big shiny shell in the water. When I went to pick it up it started to move. There was a hermit crab living inside and the shell was in its home. I picked some other shells and gave them to my sister to put on her sandcastle.

Page 70
The Tale of the Missing Bananas
The monkey was angry. He was beating his chest and jumping up and down. Someone had stolen all his bananas.
   "It's not fair," he said.
   All the animals gathered around.
   "Are you sure you didn't eat them?" asked the zebra.
   The monkey shook his head.
   "When did you last see them?" squawked the parrot.
   The monkey scratched his chin.
   "My large eyes might help me find them," said the owl.
   Suddenly, there was a loud bang. Everyone turned to see what had happened. The elephant was lying on his back. His legs were kicking in the air.
   "I slipped on a banana peel!" the elephant grumbled.

Answers

"Look, there's more of them and they lead into the jungle," said the owl.

"Come on," said the monkey.
"Let's follow the trail."

Page 72
1. When Dinosaurs Attack!
2. Escape from Wizard Mountain.
3. The Owls of the Forest.
From left to right: My Neighbor Is a Zombie! Robo Captain Saves the Day.

Page 73
Uluru, also known as Ayer's Rock, is a large sandstone rock formation in Australia.

Uluru is very important to the Aboriginal people of Australia because they believe it was created by their ancestor spirits.

The rock stands more than 1,000 feet above sea level (that's higher than the Eiffel Tower in France!) and can be seen for many miles around.

At the bottom of Uluru, there are caves with rock paintings as well as lots of bats!

Page 74
1. The bus never came, so we took a taxi instead.
2. It was cloudy and foggy, yet we still went to the park.
3. I was just about to fall asleep, when I heard a loud bang.
4. Yasin wants to buy a new game, but he can't decide which one.
5. Hannah threw the ball, and her dog chased after it.

Page 75
Although it was raining, we went out for a walk.
Charlotte couldn't finish the puzzle because a piece was missing.
After we watch the movie, we are going to get pizza.

I quickly looked for my school bag, while the teacher waited.
While he was checking his spelling, Joe spotted a few mistakes.
When the lion woke up, he gave a loud roar!

Page 76
I heard the news, later that day.
You can't enter the stadium, unless you have a ticket.
Luke went to bed because he was tired.
I watched the football game, while I ate a hot dog.

Page 77
1. As soon as it stops raining, I am going to go out and play because I need some fresh air.
2. Unless Mila gets her allowance, she cannot buy the new dress because she doesn't have enough money.
3. Although he was very tired, Yasin could not sleep while the storm was raging.
4. When Emily saw the Spooky Forest Maze, she decided she could not go in unless someone else went with her.

Page 78
Talisa Mitchell
68 Pearl Gardens
Miami, FL 33145

Kadeem Nelson
11 Rosewater Falls
Chicago, IL 60034

Page 79
1. Inside the chest was a bag of gold, a sparkling gem, a rusty key, and an old map.
2. I put the pencil, the eraser, the crayons, and the ruler back into my pencil case.
Items in the suitcase:
a toothbrush, a beach ball,
an alarm clock, shoes, and
a teddy bear.

Page 80
1. Gretel gasped, "The cottage is made of candy!"
2. The wolf growled, "All the better to see you with."
3. Jack said, "I am going to plant the magic beans."
4. Cinderella cried, "I must be home before midnight!"
5. The dwarf laughed, "Our home has never been so tidy!"

Page 81
1. "If you believe," said Peter, "then you will be able to fly!"
2. "By sticking to the path," said Wendy, "we can't get lost."
3. "They are only kids," grumbled the pirate, "so they can't beat us."
4. "I might be small," the fairy giggled, "but I'm still smarter than you are!"
5. "Don't get too close," warned the mermaid, "or else I'll splash you with my tail!"

Page 82
Possible answers include:
The frog said if he gets a kiss, he will become a prince.
Icarus boasted he will make himself wings and fly like a bird.
The fairy said that good thoughts are as bright as sunbeams.
"Grandma is a wolf," Scarlet said to everyone.
"You have three wishes," the Genie told Aladdin.
"You are too slow," teased the hare to the tortoise.

Page 83
"Your puny life is over, Human," said the alien. "And your spaceship is now mine!"

"Actually, it's my mom's ship," said Kid Phoenix. "I can't give you what is hers."

"Are you questioning me?" squealed the alien. "What is hers is now mine!"

"I don't think so," laughed Phoenix. "Besides, our plan is much better than yours."

"Hardly. My space fleet has its blasters aimed at your planet," sneered the alien.

"And our candy cannon just turned yours into marshmallow," grinned Phoenix. "So, eat that, alien!"

Page 84
1. Luke's ball went over the wall.
2. The ball smashed Mrs. Baker's window.
3. She screamed and woke up her neighbor's dog.
4. The dog went barking into Mr. Nelson's garden.
5. His cat gave a screech and jumped into Miss Clemons' tree.
6. "What is all this racket?" complained Luke's mom.

Page 85
1. girls'. 2. women's.
3. parents'. 4. Peoples'.
5. animals'. 6. teachers'.
7. waiters'. 8. babies'.

Page 86
will not; could not; do not; it is; would not; does not; should not; can not.

Page 87
don't, It's, there's, can't, it's, wouldn't.

Page 88
Possible answers include:
There is a lot of traffic. I'm going to miss my first class.
Bella is not coming on the trip anymore.
It would be good if we could have a sleepover at my place.
What are you doing next Saturday?

Page 89
1. spell. 2. possible. 3. unwell.
4. disagreeable. 5. well.
6. impossible. 7. agreeable.
8. misspell.

From left to right: unlock, disown, impolite, misstep.

Pages 90–91
hopeless, planning, finally, biggest, nervous, excited, encouragement, courageous, successful, arrived, traveled, explored, collected, proudly, planted, returned, happiness, rejoicing.

Page 92
From left to right: thumb–503; thread–502; thorn–501; thirsty--501; thrilling–502; thank–500; text–500; thief–500; think–501; thud–503.

Page 93
hurricane—a violent storm with heavy wind and rain.
catapult—a machine used to throw objects.
comet—an object in space made of dust and gas.
summit—the highest part of something.
zither—a stringed instrument.
inhabit—to live in a place.
gadget—a clever tool or device.
mammoth—a large extinct elephant.
Possible answers include:
population—the number of people living in a place (country, city, town).
deciduous—trees and shrubs that shed their leaves.
omnivore—an animal or person that eats both meat and plant foods.

Page 94
1. agreed. 2. best. 3. plan. 4. fear.
5. angry.

Page 95
Possible answers include:
(best) greatest; (moved) swam; (red) crimson; (said) boasted; (said) laughed; (big) large; (came) burst; (a lot) hundreds;

(very big) enormous; (said) screeched; (went) dived; (hole) crack; (upset) furious; (went) swam; (said) hooted.

Page 96
1. louder. 2. better. 3. healthier.
4. slower. 5. taller. 6. hotter.

Page 97
1. brightest. 2. coldest. 3. longest.
4. heaviest.
Highest mountain–Mount Everest; Biggest lake–Lake Superior.

Page 99
From left to right: spotless, frosty, break, relaxed.
Possible answers include: loud–thunderous, noisy, deafening; friend–pal, companion, buddy.

Page 101
Possible answers include:
1. boing. 2. squelch. 3. screech.
4. fizz. 5. creak. 6. bang.

Page 102
cold, small, soft, off, disagree.

Page 103
Possible answers from left to right include: cookies, toffee, peach, marshmallow.

Reading, Comprehension, and Writing

Page 106–107
Possible answers include: kind, strong, courageous, skilled, good.

Page 108
Possible answers include:
1. Improve their homes. 2. Make a fire. 3. Find meat for their winter stores. 2. It's not fair that I am doing everything.
Flimsy—something that is weak and fragile.

Answers

Page 109

Possible answers include:
Maushop uses his tremendous strength to pull up the trees.
(sad) (frustrated)
Maushop wanted the tribe to do things for themselves.
Best definition of self-sufficient—2. to look after yourself without needing help.

Pages 110–111

1. King Minos asks Daedalus to create a maze.
2. Daedalus designs a complex maze. He calls it the labyrinth.
3. Daedalus and Icarus become prisoners.
4. Icarus collects feathers for his father.
5. Daedalus makes two pairs of wings.
6. Icarus is warned not to fly too close to the sun.
7. Daedalus and Icarus use their wings to escape the island of Crete.
8. The sun melts the wax on Icarus's wings.
9. Icarus falls from the sky and plunges into the sea.

Pages 112–113

false, true, false, true, true, true.
Possible answers include:
arching—curved, bent; hardy—strong, tough; nutritious—healthy, nourishing.

Page 114

Possible answers include:
You should treat others as you would like to be treated.
Don't play tricks on others if you don't want the same treatment.

Page 115

Possible answers include:
1. sneaky, sly, cunning, clever, devious, wily.
2. friendly, sad, hungry, clever.

3. Because she did not like the mean trick the fox had played on her.
4. The fox was angry because he couldn't reach the soup with his short snout.

Pages 118–119

Possible answers include:
1. Mary Meek because she would like to solve a mystery or save the day.
2. Greta Gump because she is always in trouble and likes to bully people.
3. boastful—Greta; imaginative—Mary; shy—Mary; angry—Greta.

Page 120

Possible answers include: spooky, dark, creepy, gloomy, scary, mysterious, eerie, frightening.

Page 121

Possible answers include:
(monster)—I wish I was a scary monster; (clown)—I want to be able to juggle.

Page 124

Sentences that should be underlined are: He is catching flies with his long sticky tongue. He is feeling happy. Frog quickly hops from lily pad to lily pad. Frog sees an elephant wading into the water. He lifts up his trunk and trumpets loudly.

Page 125

Possible answers include: house made of sticks; old mother hen; little chicks six; "Cluck," said the mother; "We cluck," said the six; So they clucked; house made of sticks; old mother owl; little owlets seven; "Hoot," said the mother; "We hoot," said the seven; So they hooted.

Pages 126–127

1. Owl/fowl, sing/ring, married/tarried, away/day, grows/nose, wood/stood, nose/nose, willing/shilling, will/hill, away/day, mince/quince, spoon/moon, hand/sand, moon/moon.
2. The owl is elegant and can sing sweetly.
3. Too long we have tarried.
4. The ring in the pig's nose.
5. fruit.
6. The characters are talking animals. The poem is funny and does not make sense.

Page 130

1. nonfiction, 2. fiction, 3. nonfiction, 4. fiction, 5. nonfiction, 6. nonfiction.
1. The Magic Carpet. 2. All about Space. 3. Safe Cycling.

Page 131

1. Because we learn new facts every day.
2. Eight planets.
3. Jupiter, Saturn, Uranus, and Neptune.
4. Mars.
5. Jupiter.

Pages 132–133

Possible answers include:
1. Born in 1797 on a farm in the state of New York.
2. Both her parents were slaves.
3. Refuge means a place of safety.
4. To get her son back.
5. She was an excellent speaker.
6. She taught people about slavery and what it was like to be a slave. She dedicated her life to ending slavery. We can admire her courage for speaking out for what she believed in.

Pages 134–135

1. Possible title—Fastest Land Animals
2. a. kangaroo, b. jackrabbit, c. lion, d. antelope, e. cheetah.
3. a. miles per hour; b. cheetah;

c. antelope; d. leaps and zigzags quickly; e. jackrabbit and kangaroo; f. It gives an easy and quick way to compare the speed of the animals.

Page 136
l. Splash Canyon. 2. Spooky Forest. 3. Planet X. 4. Future Zone. 5. Enchanted Valley. 6. Pirate Cove.

Page 137
l. The human body is an amazing machine.
2. Every organ has a special job to do. Your skeleton protects your vital organs.
3. Possible title—Our Amazing Body!

Page 138
l. 10; 2. 23; 3. 14; 4. 6.

Page 139
Possible answers include:
defense—for protection.
tentacles—a long, slender limb.
prey—an animal that is hunted for food.
predators—an animal that eats other animals.
species—a group of animals that have common features.

Pages 141
l. a. true, b. false, c. true, d. true.
2. Worker bees build the hive, protect the hive, and collect nectar and pollen from flowers.
3. Bees are important because they produce honey and they pollinate flowers, which produce fruit and vegetables for us.
4. Worker bees perform a waggle dance to tell other bees where to find flowers that have lots of nectar and pollen. The bees need this nectar and pollen to make food.

Page 142
l. First, the female butterfly lays her eggs on a leaf.
2. After about 5 days, an egg will hatch into a small caterpillar.
3. The caterpillar must eat a lot of leaves in order to grow.
4. After a few weeks, the caterpillar surrounds its body with a hard shell called a chrysalis.
5. Inside the chrysalis, the caterpillar slowly changes into a butterfly.
6. When the butterfly is ready to emerge, the chrysalis splits open.
7. Finally, the butterfly must wait for its wings to dry out before it can fly away.

Page 143
The Galapagos Islands are a group of 19 islands in the pacific Ocean. They lie off the west coast of South america. They were made from active volcanoes and the the largest is called Sierra Negra on the island of Isabela. The islands are famous for there many native animals, such as marine iguanas, penguins, sea lions, and Giant Tortoises.

Page 144
Paragraph order: l, 4, 2, 3, 5.

Page 146
Equipment: baking tray.
Ingredients: bar of chocolate.
l. Peel the bananas.
4. Pour the plain yogurt into a jug.
5. Lay the banana lollipops on the baking paper.
6. Put the tray in the freezer for an hour.
8. Dip the end of each banana lollipop in the chocolate.

Page 148–149
Cats make better pets than dogs.
l. Cats don't need to be taken for walks.
2. You don't have to wash a cat.
3. Cats don't make a lot of noise.
a. Dogs can get dirty and smelly.
c. Cats like to purr softly.
d. Dogs need to be walked, even in bad weather.

Page 152
l. shoes, 2. dog biscuits, 3. cereal, 4. perfume, 5. ring.

Number Skills

Page 156
$264 = 200 + 60 + 4$,
$382 = 300 + 80 + 2$,
$401 = 400 + 0 + 1$,
$890 = 800 + 90 + 0$,
$637 = 600 + 30 + 7$,
$762 = 700 + 60 + 2$.

Page 157
Descending order: 90, 80, 73, 64, 56, 38, 22, 10.
Ascending order: 5, 29, 36, 40, 55, 74, 82, 98.

Page 158
The nearest ten: 45 → 50, 41 → 40, 67 → 70, 76 → 80, 89 → 90, 12 → 10, 54 → 50.

Page 159
The nearest hundred:
167 → 200, 275 → 300, 820 → 800.

Page 160
twenty 20, thirty-six 36, sixty-four 64, eighty-six 86, ninety-five 95.

Page 161
$20 + 70 = 90$, $200 + 700 = 900$.
$5 + 4 = 9$, $50 + 40 = 90$,
$500 + 400 = 900$.
$80 - 30 = 50$, $800 - 300 = 500$.
$9 - 5 = 4$, $90 - 50 = 40$,
$900 - 500 = 400$.

Page 162
$10 - 4 = 6$, $10 - 6 = 4$;
$15 - 7 = 8$, $15 - 8 = 7$;

Answers

21 − 6 = 15, 21 − 15 = 6;
29 − 7 = 22, 29 − 22 = 7;
40 − 2 = 38, 40 − 38 = 2;
59 − 8 = 51, 59 − 51 = 8.

Page 163
1. 15 points difference;
2. Liam's total: 60;
3. Kelly's final total: 25;
4. Nizra's total: 105;
5. 80 points difference.

Page 164
Pairs that make 100 are:
25 + 75, 31 + 69, 82 + 18,
55 + 45, 64 + 36, 59 + 41.

Page 165
17 + 17: double 7 = 14,
double 10 = 20, total = 34.
26 + 26: double 6 = 12,
double 20 = 40, total = 52.
49 + 49: double 9 = 18,
double 40 = 80, total = 98.
35 + 35: double 5 = 10,
double 30 = 60, total =70.

Page 166
34 + 36 = (30 + 30) + (4 + 6) = 60 + 10 = 70,
55 + 29 = (50 + 20) + (5 + 9) = 70 + 14 = 84,
62 + 38 = (60 + 30) + (2 + 8) = 90 + 10 = 100,
77 + 24 = (70 + 20) + (7 + 4) = 90 + 11 = 101.

Page 167

84 − 55 = 29

73 − 43 = 30

98 − 67 = 31

Page 168
From left to right: 179, 289, 577, 783, 687, 948.

Page 169
From left to right: 390, 542, 792, 754, 610, 421.

Page 170
From left to right: 245, 310, 117, 652, 841, 114.

Page 171
From left to right: 348, 634, 120, 244, 745, 718.

Page 172
5 + 5 + 5 = 15,
3 groups of 5 = 15, 3 x 5 = 15.
4 groups of 3, 4 x 3 = 12.
3 groups of 10, 3 x 10 = 30.
5 groups of 5, 5 x 5 = 25.
4 groups of 4, 4 x 4 = 16.
3 groups of 6, 3 x 6 = 18.

Page 173
4 x 5 = 20, 5 x 4 = 20.
3 x 7 = 21, 7 x 3 = 21.
2 x 10 = 20, 10 x 2 = 20.

Page 174

1	2	3	4	5	6	7	8	9	10
11	12	13	14	15	16	17	18	19	20
21	22	23	24	25	26	27	28	29	30
31	32	33	34	35	36	37	38	39	40
41	42	43	44	45	46	47	48	49	50
51	52	53	54	55	56	57	58	59	60
61	62	63	64	65	66	67	68	69	70
71	72	73	74	75	76	77	78	79	80
81	82	83	84	85	86	87	88	89	90
91	92	93	94	95	96	97	98	99	100

Missing numbers are: 4, 6, 8, 12, 14, 16, 18.

Page 175

1	2	3	4	5	6	7	8	9	10
11	12	13	14	15	16	17	18	19	20
21	22	23	24	25	26	27	28	29	30
31	32	33	34	35	36	37	38	39	40
41	42	43	44	45	46	47	48	49	50
51	52	53	54	55	56	57	58	59	60
61	62	63	64	65	66	67	68	69	70
71	72	73	74	75	76	77	78	79	80
81	82	83	84	85	86	87	88	89	90
91	92	93	94	95	96	97	98	99	100

Missing numbers are: 6, 9, 15, 21, 24, 30.

Page 176

1	2	3	4	5	6	7	8	9	10
11	12	13	14	15	16	17	18	19	20
21	22	23	24	25	26	27	28	29	30
31	32	33	34	35	36	37	38	39	40
41	42	43	44	45	46	47	48	49	50
51	52	53	54	55	56	57	58	59	60
61	62	63	64	65	66	67	68	69	70
71	72	73	74	75	76	77	78	79	80
81	82	83	84	85	86	87	88	89	90
91	92	93	94	95	96	97	98	99	100

Missing numbers are: 8, 16, 24, 28, 36.

Page 177

1	2	3	4	5	6	7	8	9	10
11	12	13	14	15	16	17	18	19	20
21	22	23	24	25	26	27	28	29	30
31	32	33	34	35	36	37	38	39	40
41	42	43	44	45	46	47	48	49	50
51	52	53	54	55	56	57	58	59	60
61	62	63	64	65	66	67	68	69	70
71	72	73	74	75	76	77	78	79	80
81	82	83	84	85	86	87	88	89	90
91	92	93	94	95	96	97	98	99	100

Missing numbers are: 10, 15, 25, 35, 40, 45.

Page 178

1	2	3	4	5	6	7	8	9	10
11	12	13	14	15	16	17	18	19	20
21	22	23	24	25	26	27	28	29	30
31	32	33	34	35	36	37	38	39	40
41	42	43	44	45	46	47	48	49	50
51	52	53	54	55	56	57	58	59	60
61	62	63	64	65	66	67	68	69	70
71	72	73	74	75	76	77	78	79	80
81	82	83	84	85	86	87	88	89	90
91	92	93	94	95	96	97	98	99	100

Missing numbers are: 12, 18, 30, 42, 48, 60.

Page 179

1	2	3	4	5	6	7	8	9	10
11	12	13	14	15	16	17	18	19	20
21	22	23	24	25	26	27	28	29	30
31	32	33	34	35	36	37	38	39	40
41	42	43	44	45	46	47	48	49	50
51	52	53	54	55	56	57	58	59	60
61	62	63	64	65	66	67	68	69	70
71	72	73	74	75	76	77	78	79	80
81	82	83	84	85	86	87	88	89	90
91	92	93	94	95	96	97	98	99	100

Missing numbers are: 14, 21, 35, 49, 70.

Page 180

1	2	3	4	5	6	7	8	9	10
11	12	13	14	15	16	17	18	19	20
21	22	23	24	25	26	27	28	29	30
31	32	33	34	35	36	37	38	39	40
41	42	43	44	45	46	47	48	49	50
51	52	53	54	55	56	57	58	59	60
61	62	63	64	65	66	67	68	69	70
71	72	73	74	75	76	77	78	79	80
81	82	83	84	85	86	87	88	89	90
91	92	93	94	95	96	97	98	99	100

Missing numbers are: 16, 24, 40, 64, 80.

Page 181

1	2	3	4	5	6	7	8	9	10
11	12	13	14	15	16	17	18	19	20
21	22	23	24	25	26	27	28	29	30
31	32	33	34	35	36	37	38	39	40
41	42	43	44	45	46	47	48	49	50
51	52	53	54	55	56	57	58	59	60
61	62	63	64	65	66	67	68	69	70
71	72	73	74	75	76	77	78	79	80
81	82	83	84	85	86	87	88	89	90
91	92	93	94	95	96	97	98	99	100

Missing numbers are: 18, 36, 54, 72, 90.

Page 182

1	2	3	4	5	6	7	8	9	10
11	12	13	14	15	16	17	18	19	20
21	22	23	24	25	26	27	28	29	30
31	32	33	34	35	36	37	38	39	40
41	42	43	44	45	46	47	48	49	50
51	52	53	54	55	56	57	58	59	60
61	62	63	64	65	66	67	68	69	70
71	72	73	74	75	76	77	78	79	80
81	82	83	84	85	86	87	88	89	90
91	92	93	94	95	96	97	98	99	100

Missing numbers are: 20, 30, 40, 60, 70, 80, 100

Page 183

0	1	2	3	4	5	6	7	8	9	10
1	1	2	3	4	5	6	7	8	9	10
2	2	4	6	8	10	12	14	16	18	20
3	3	6	9	12	15	18	21	24	27	30
4	4	8	12	16	20	24	28	32	36	40
5	5	10	15	20	25	30	35	40	45	50
6	6	12	18	24	30	36	42	48	54	60
7	7	14	21	28	35	42	49	56	63	70
8	8	16	24	32	40	48	56	64	72	80
9	9	18	27	36	45	54	63	72	81	90
10	10	20	30	40	50	60	70	80	90	100

7 x 6 = 42, 8 x 4 = 32,
9 x 3 = 27, 8 x 9 = 72,
5 x 5 = 25, 8 x 8 = 64.

Page 184

1. 12 stickers, 2. 49 days,
3. $12, 4. 32 books,
5. 27 cupcakes, 6. 30 bananas.

Page 185

Left to right: 70 + 28 = 98,
80 + 8 = 88, 150 + 10 = 160,
120 + 21 = 141, 450 + 9 = 459,
120 + 4 = 124.

Page 186

18 ÷ 3 = 6, 9 ÷ 3 = 3,
12 ÷ 6 = 2, 16 ÷ 4 = 4,
18 ÷ 9 = 2, 20 ÷ 4 = 5.

Page 187

20 ÷ 4 = 5, 30 ÷ 5 = 6,
36 ÷ 6 = 6.

Page 188

1. 4 lengths, 2. 4 in each team,
3. 4 red tiles, 4. 1 bone left over,
5. 6 balloons each, 2 left over,
6. 3 miles.

Page 189

12 ÷ 4 = 3, 12 ÷ 3 = 4,
75 ÷ 3 = 25, 75 ÷ 25 = 3,
30 ÷ 2 = 15, 30 ÷ 15 = 2,
100 ÷ 2 = 50, 100 ÷ 50 = 2,
60 ÷ 3 = 20, 60 ÷ 20 = 3,
200 ÷ 4 = 50, 200 ÷ 50 = 4.

Page 190

¹4	²6		³2	0	0
	0			5	
⁴9		⁵2		⁶3	5
0		⁷8	1		
	⁸9			⁹1	8
		¹⁰1	5	0	

Page 191

Boulders to be colored are:
6, 24, 21, 33, 15, 12, 30.

Page 192

42, 64, 30, 27, 3, 8, 10, 7, 20.

Answers

Page 193
6, 9, 4, 7.

Page 194
From left to right: 12 ÷ 2 = 6,
27 ÷ 3, 49 ÷ 7 = 7, 25 ÷ 5 = 5,
64 ÷ 8, 81 ÷ 9, 90 ÷ 10, 63 ÷ 9.
Using your own numbers,
you could have:
6 ÷ 1, 12 ÷ 2, 18 ÷ 3, 24 ÷ 4, 36 ÷ 6.
There are many other possible
answers.

Page 195
From left to right: 24 ÷ 2,
36 ÷ 6 = 6, 3 x 3 = 9,
4 x 1 = 4, 4 x 2 = 8, 33 ÷ 3 = 11,
Using your own numbers,
you could have:
6 x 2, 24 ÷ 2, 3 x 4, 12 ÷ 1, 36 ÷ 3.
There are many other possible
answers.

Page 196
From left to right: 99, 328, 59, 186,
148, 305, 320, 279.

Page 197
From left to right: 72, 136, 275,
231, 267, 170, 336, 388, 138.

Page 198
From left to right: 4, 4, 6, 3, 7, 10,
5, 3, 3.

Page 199
From left to right: 4 r 2, 6 r 1,
7 r 2, 3 r 1, 2 r 3, 4 r 1, 6 r 4,
6 r 1, 3 r 1.

Page 200
1. 35 balls,
2. 15 children,
3. 12 pairs,
4. 7 books,
5. 5 pizzas,
6. 2 cupcakes each and
1 left over.

Page 201
Missing numbers in order from
the top: 20, 5, 4, 5, 8, 4, 6.

Page 202
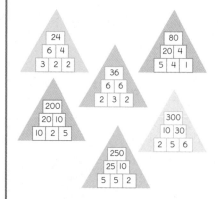

Page 203

Fractions, Shapes, and Area

Page 206

Page 207

Page 208

Page 209

4 cookies should be colored.

Page 210
6 apples should be circled,
$\frac{1}{2}$ of 12 = 6.

3 cones should be circled,
$\frac{1}{4}$ of 12 = 3.

4 drinks should be circled,
$\frac{1}{3}$ of 12 = 4.

Page 211
3 balloons,
$\frac{1}{6}$ of 12 = 2, 2 leaves,
$\frac{1}{8}$ of 8 = 1, 1 carrot.

Page 212
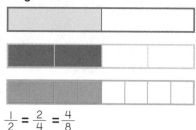

$\frac{1}{2} = \frac{2}{4} = \frac{4}{8}$

Page 213
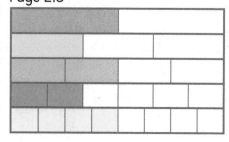

$\frac{1}{2} > \frac{1}{3}$　　$\frac{1}{2} = \frac{2}{4}$

$\frac{1}{2} = \frac{3}{6}$　　$\frac{1}{3} < \frac{2}{3}$

$\frac{1}{4} > \frac{1}{8}$　　$\frac{1}{4} = \frac{2}{8}$

$\frac{1}{2} = \frac{4}{8}$　　$\frac{2}{6} < \frac{4}{8}$

Page 214
4 pieces, 6 candies, 3 red flowers, 6 yellow flowers.

Page 215
14 parrots, 16 seagulls, 18 penguins.

Pages 216–217
$\frac{2}{4}$, $\frac{2}{3}$, $\frac{5}{6}$, $\frac{4}{8}$, $\frac{4}{8}$

Page 218
From left to right:
$\frac{5}{6}$, $\frac{4}{8}$, $\frac{3}{8}$, $\frac{3}{6}$, $\frac{7}{8}$.

Page 219
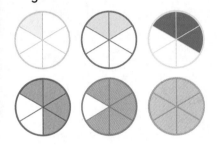

Page 220
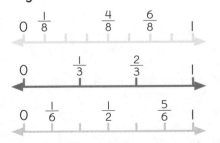

$0 \quad \frac{1}{3} \quad \frac{2}{3} \quad \frac{3}{3} = 1$

$0 \quad \frac{1}{6} \quad \frac{2}{6} \quad \frac{3}{6} \quad \frac{4}{6} \quad \frac{5}{6} \quad \frac{6}{6} = 1$

$0 \quad \frac{1}{8} \quad \frac{2}{8} \quad \frac{3}{8} \quad \frac{4}{8} \quad \frac{5}{8} \quad \frac{6}{8} \quad \frac{7}{8} \quad \frac{8}{8} = 1$

Page 221

$0 \quad \frac{1}{8} \quad \frac{4}{8} \quad \frac{6}{8} \quad 1$

$0 \quad \frac{1}{3} \quad \frac{2}{3} \quad 1$

$0 \quad \frac{1}{6} \quad \frac{1}{2} \quad \frac{5}{6} \quad 1$

Pages 222-223
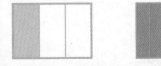

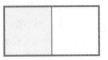 

Page 224
$\frac{4}{8} = \frac{1}{2} = \frac{2}{4} = \frac{3}{6}$, $\frac{1}{3} = \frac{2}{6}$,
$\frac{2}{8} = \frac{1}{4}$, $\frac{6}{8} = \frac{3}{4}$.

Page 225
$\frac{1}{4} < \frac{1}{2}$, 3 pieces **>** 2 pieces,
$\frac{1}{2}$ of 2 pints = 1 pint **<** $\frac{1}{3}$ of
9 pints = 3 pints

Page 226
5, 6, 7, 4.

Page 227
From left to right: 15 ÷ 3 = 5,
16 ÷ 8 = 2, 30 ÷ 3 = 10, 32 ÷ 8 = 4,
18 ÷ 6 = 3, 40 ÷ 4 = 10, 36 ÷ 6 = 6,
50 ÷ 2 = 25.

Page 228
$\frac{3}{4}$ are white, $\frac{2}{3}$ are from Zag,
$\frac{2}{6}$ are unfriendly, $\frac{5}{8}$ do not go on
a space walk.

Page 229
6, 4, 2; 8, 4, 2.

Page 230
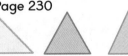

1. red. 2. blue. 3. green.

Page 231
square: 4 equal sides, rhombus: opposite angles are equal, rectangle: opposite sides are equal.
1. rectangle. 2. square. 3. rhombus.

Page 232
parallelogram: opposite angles are equal,
trapezoid: has 2 parallel sides,
kite: sides next to each other are the same.

Page 233
Any shape with 4 straight sides is a quadrilateral.

Page 234
pentagon, hexagon, the US Pentagon is shaped like a pentagon, honeycomb cells are hexagons.

Page 235
From left to right: pentagon, hexagon, pentagon, hexagon.

Page 236
regular heptagon: 7 equal sides, regular octagon: 8 equal sides.

Page 237
From left to right: square, octagon, trapezoid, hexagon, parallelogram, triangle, kite, pentagon, rhombus, rectangle.

S	O	C	T	A	G	O	N	C	B	M	X	M
C	V	K	R	E	L	G	N	A	T	C	E	R
N	O	G	A	T	N	E	P	Z	T	S	R	K
C	S	G	H	Q	U	Z	P	H	N	G	R	D
D	F	Q	J	K	A	V	D	E	L	L	W	Y
T	Y	U	U	X	M	K	P	X	R	T	L	R
K	R	U	J	A	M	I	S	A	W	R	P	H
H	X	I	X	Z	R	T	J	G	J	N	Y	O
P	A	R	A	L	L	E	L	O	G	R	A	M
S	D	Y	Q	N	H	R	B	N	G	Y	S	B
X	H	D	U	Y	G	D	V	N	S	P	H	U
C	K	P	W	W	C	L	B	M	K	M	R	S
P	L	R	T	R	A	P	E	Z	O	I	D	J

Answers

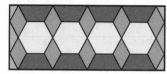

Page 239
l. circle. 2. oval. 3. semicircle. 4. circle.

Page 240
l. triangular prism. 2. cube.
3. cone. 4. cuboid. 5. cylinder.
6. pyramid. 7. sphere.

Page 241
cube, triangular prism,
cuboid, pyramid.

Page 242
4 cubes, **9** cubes.
l. triangle. 2. parallelogram,
3. rectangle, 4. parallelogram.

Page 243
Left to right: 6, 8, l0, l2, ll, l5.

Page 244
Left to right: 8, 8, l2, 6, l2, l0.

Page 245
length 4 squares, width 2 squares.
length 5, width 3,
area l5 square units.
length 8, width 2,
area l6 square units.
length 7, width 4,
area 28 square units.
length 8, width 3,
area 24 square units.

Page 246
3 x 3 = 9 square units,
5 x 3 = l5 square units,
6 x 2 = l2 square units,
4 x 3 = l2 square units.

Page 247
2 x 2 = 4, 4 x 2 = 8,
total area = l2 square units.
6 x 2 = l2, 8 x l = 8,
total area = 20 square units.
5 x 3 = l5, 2 x 2 = 4,
total area = l9 square units.

Page 248
The garden: 5 x 4 = 20 square feet.
The pool: 20 x l0 = 200 square feet.
The carpet: l4 x l0 = l40 and
l2 x l0 = l20, total 260 square feet.

Pages 250–251
Left to right: l8 units, l2 units,
l2 units, l5 units, l8 units, l6 units.

Pages 252–253
5, l6 units.
Left to right: l5 units, l6 units,
l6 units, 22 units, 30 units.

Measurement, Data, and Money

Page 256
Left to right: 1:10, 10 minutes past l;
4:45, quarter to 5 or 45 minutes
past 4; 7:55, 5 minutes to 8 or
55 minutes past 7.

Page 257
55 minutes, 35 minutes,
20 minutes, 45 minutes.

Page 258
Left to right: 7:18, l8 minutes
past 7; 8:26, 26 minutes past 8;
2:57, 3 minutes to 3 or 57 minutes
past 2; l0:32, 28 minutes to ll or
32 minutes past l0; ll:46,
l4 minutes to l2 or 46 minutes
past ll.

Page 259
2. l:15 p.m., 3. 6:50 p.m., 4. 5:15 p.m.

Page 260
Left to right: 4 minutes past 2,
22 minutes past 3, 2 minutes to ll
or 58 minutes past l0, 25 minutes
to l0 or 35 minutes past 9, 20
minutes to 8 or 40 minutes past 7,
20 minutes past 5.

Page 261
3:00 p.m., l0:00 a.m., 5:00 a.m.,
4:30 a.m.

Page 262
l. 65 minutes, 2. 90 minutes,
3. 24 hours, 4. 75 seconds.

Page 263
l. 7:15 p.m., 2. 3:05 p.m.,
3. l0:30 p.m., 4. 4:30 p.m.

Page 264
8:20 ➡ 8.25,
7:35 ➡ 7:40,
3:40 ➡ 3:45,
l0:25 ➡ l0:30,
ll:55 ➡ l2:00.

Page 265

Page 266
l. 8:30, 2. 2:05, 3. 7:15, 4. l0:20,
5. 9:05, 6. 3:15, 7. l2.30, 8. 5:35.

Page 267
l. 3l days, 2. Wednesday,
3. l9th of July, 4. l5th of July,
5. 23rd of July, 6. Wednesday.

Page 268
Left to right: cherries—ounces,
baby—pounds, bus—tons,
suitcase—pounds, candy—ounces,
elephant - tons.

Page 269
✘: The banana weighs the most.
✔: Correct.
✘: The banana weighs 20 g more
than the grapes.
✔: Correct.
✔: Correct.
✘: The grapes and a banana
would weigh l60 g.
✔: Correct.
✘: $\frac{1}{2}$ kg = 500 g

Page 270
7 oz, 4 oz, 8 oz, 4 oz.

Page 271

socks = 3 oz, apple = 5 oz, car = 1 t,
dog = 20 lb, book = 1 lb 12 oz.
3 pairs of socks = 9 oz, 4 apples = 20
oz, 6 cupcakes = 24 oz.

Page 272

Left to right: $\frac{1}{2}$ cup,

2 cups or 1 pint,

3 cups or $1\frac{1}{2}$ pints,

4 cups or 2 pints or 1 quart.

Page 273

Left to right: bathtub–gallons,
can of soda–cups, pond–gallons,
cauldron–gallons, bucket–quarts,
medicine bottle–ounces,
gas tank–gallons.

Page 274

A is three-quarters full.
A and C total one liter.
We would expect a glass to hold
less than a liter.
We would expect a teapot
to hold 1 liter.

Page 275

1. 6 teaspoons, 2. 300 ml,
3. 990 ml, 4. 10 glasses,
5. 2 bottles.

Page 276

$2\frac{1}{2}$ inches, $3\frac{1}{4}$ inches.

Page 277

You can check your own answers.

Page 278

A = $1\frac{3}{4}$ inches, B = $2\frac{1}{2}$ inches,

C = 3 inches, B = $\frac{1}{2}$ inch shorter

than C, D = 1 inch longer than C.

Page 279

key–less, frog–less, garden fork–
more, tennis racket–less,
road bridge–more, carrot–less,
crane–less, Earth–more,
swimming pool–less.

Page 280

4 cm, 8 cm, 11 cm.
Your height–centimeters,
foot–centimeters,
pencil–centimeters,
bedroom–meters.
Distance to your nearest
town/cityv kilometers.

Page 281

1. 50 cm tall, 2. 15 cm taller,
3. 12 cm shorter, 4. 30 cm long.

Page 282

Ask a parent to check your
measurements for this activity.

Page 283

Whole squares = 8,
half squares = 10,
8 + 5 = 13 square units.

Page 284

Perimeter of the green shape =
8 units.
Area of the green shape = 3 units.
Perimeter of the blue shape = 8 units.
Area of the blue shape = 4 units.
The blue shape has the biggest area.
The blue shape would make the
biggest field.

Page 285

Perimeter of the yellow shape =
10 units.
Area of the yellow shape = 6 units.
Perimeter of the red shape = 14 units.
Area of the red shape = 6 units.
The red shape has the
biggest perimeter.
The red shape would need the
most fencing because it is longer
and narrower.

Page 286

1. burger 8, pizza 9, pasta 5,
sandwich 6, salad 3.
2. 8 burgers,
3. 4 more pizzas were sold,
4. pizza was the most popular,
5. 31 sales in total.

Page 287

1. soda sold the most,
2. 6 fewer coffees were sold,
3. milkshake and orange juice sold
equally well,
4. 12 altogether,
5. 26 drinks sold altogether.

Page 288

1. 9 students, 2. snake, 3. chimpanzee,
4. 5 preferred penguins,
5. 2 more preferred elephants.

Page 289

Ask a parent to check your graph.

Page 290

45 cents, 35 cents, 27 cents, 50 cents.

Page 291

75 cents, 60 cents, 66 cents,
100 cents (1 dollar).

Page 292

A. 95 cents, B. 75 cents,
C. 100 cents, D. 90 cents.
Purse C has one dollar.

Page 293

50 + 20 = 70 cents,
30 + 60 = 90 cents,
20 + 20 + 30 = 70 cents,
30 + 20 + 50 = 100 cents = 1 dollar.

Page 294

Page 295

1. 4 pencils, 2. 50 cents, 3. 6 balls,
4. 19 cents, 5. 10 balloons.

Answers

Page 296

70¢	25¢ 10¢
80¢	25¢ 5¢
50¢	10¢ 5¢
65¢	25¢ 25¢
85¢	10¢ 10¢

Page 297
1. 160 cents,
2. 2 dollars,
3. 120 cents,
4. 3 dollars 60 cents,
5. 100 cents.

Page 298
1. 5 cents, 2. 10 cents, 3. 50 cents,
4. 100 cents, 5. 10 cents.

Page 299
$1.05, $1.30, $1.20, $3.05.

Page 300
$1.40, $2.21, $3.25, $4.01.

Page 301
1. 30 cents, 2. 25 cents,
3. 50 cents, 4. 1dollar 10 cents,
5. 20 cents.

Page 302
apple = 10,
pear = 7,
orange = 4.
apple + pear + orange = 21.
strawberry = 6,
banana = 4,
lemon = 10.
strawberry + banana + lemon = 20.

Page 303
bee = 5,
butterfly = 20,
ladybug = 4.
bee + butterfly + ladybug = 29.
hat = 30,
gloves = 15,
socks = 5.
hat + gloves + socks = 50.

Page 304–305

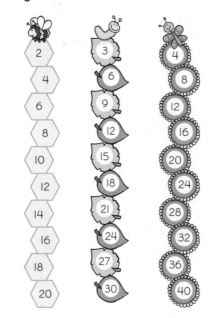

Page 306
Ask a parent to check how many rectangles and triangles you have drawn.

320